34/6/1

IGMacdonald

November 1963

DIFFERENTIAL GEOMETRY

A. V. POGORELOV

DIFFERENTIAL GEOMETRY

Translated from the First Russian Edition
by

LEO F. BORON
The Pennsylvania State University

P. NOORDHOFF N.V. - GRONINGEN - THE NETHERLANDS

CONTENTS

PART TWO

Theory of surfaces

INTRODUCTION

Differential geometry is that branch of mathematics which investigates geometric forms, primarily curves and surfaces, but also families of curves and surfaces, using methods of infinitesimal analysis. It is characteristic of differential geometry that it studies, above all, properties of curves and surfaces "in the small," i.e. the properties of arbitrarily small pieces of curves and surfaces.

Differential geometry arose and developed in close relationship with analysis which itself grew, to a significant degree, out of geometric problems. Many geometric concepts preceded the corresponding ideas in analysis. Thus, for example, the notion of a tangent preceded the concept of a derivative and the idea of area and volume preceded that of an integral.

The origin of differential geometry goes back to the first half of the eighteenth century and is associated with the names of Euler and Monge. The first comprehensive work on the theory of surfaces was Monge's *Applications of Analysis to Geometry*, 1807.

In 1827 Gauss published the work *General Investigations Concerning Curved Surfaces* which forms the basis of the theory of surfaces in its modern form. Since that time, differential geometry ceased being only an application of analysis and assumed an independent role in mathematics.

The discovery of noneuclidean geometry by Lobachevsky played an enormous role in the development of all of geometry, including differential geometry. Thus, in 1854 Riemann, by his lectures on *The Hypotheses which lie at the Foundations of Geometry*, established the foundations of so-called Riemannian geometry, which in its applications to multi-dimensional manifolds finds itself in the same relationship to the geometry of n-dimensional euclidean space as intrinsic geometry of an arbitrary surface to euclidean geometry in the plane.

Klein's group-theoretic point of view expounded in his *Erlangen Program* of 1872 was developed by Cartan in respect to applications to differential geometry; he accomplished this by constructing a theory of surfaces with projective and affine connection.

In Russia, the school of differential geometry was founded by Minding and Peterson whose basic investigations are devoted to questions of the bending of surfaces. These investigations were continued in the works of many Russian, and later Soviet, geometers.

The lectures of the author on differential geometry in the Physics-Mathematics Department of the Kharkov State University form the basic material of the present book. The author's aim is to present a rigorous discussion of the fundamentals of differential geometry and of the methods of investigation which are characteristic of this branch of mathematics, without disturbing well-established tradition in the process. A large amount of factual material concerning differential geometry has been relegated to exercises and problems, the solution of which ought to be considered obligatory for serious students of geometry.

PART ONE

THEORY OF CURVES

Chapter I

THE CONCEPT OF CURVE

A curve is one of the fundamental objects considered in differential geometry. In this chapter we shall discuss the concept of curve to the extent required in the remainder of the book.

§ 1. Elementary curve. We shall preface the definition of an elementary curve with some facts about mappings of an arbitrary set of points in (three-dimensional Euclidean) space.

Suppose M is an arbitrary set of points in space. We say that f is a given *mapping* of the set M into space if each point X in the set M is assigned some point $f(X)$ in space. The point $f(X)$ in space is called the *image* of the point X. The set of points $f(M)$, consisting of the images of all the points of the set M, is called the image of the set M.

A mapping f of the set M into space is said to be *one-to-one* and *bicontinuous* (in short, *topological*) if the following three conditions are satisfied:

1) The images of distinct points are distinct;

2) If X is an arbitrary point of the set M and X_n is a sequence of points in M which converges to X, then the sequence of points $f(X_n)$, which are the images of the X_n, converges, and moreover, it converges to the point $f(X)$ which is the image of the point X;

3) If $f(X)$ is an arbitrary point of the set $f(M)$ and $f(X_n)$ is a sequence in $f(M)$ which converges to $f(X)$, then the sequence of points X_n, corresponding to the $f(X_n)$, converges, and moreover, it converges to the point X.

If, for a mapping f of the set M, only the first condition is satisfied then the mapping f is said to be *one-to-one*; if only the second condition is satisfied, then f is said to be *continuous*.

We shall now define an elementary curve.

We shall say that a set γ of points in space is an *elementary curve* if this set is the image of an open interval on the real line under a one-to-one and bicontinuous mapping of the open interval into space.

Suppose γ is an elementary curve and let $a < t < b$ be an open interval, the image of which is a curve under the mapping f. Let $f_1(t)$, $f_2(t)$, and $f_3(t)$ be the coordinates of the point on the curve which corresponds to the point t on the open interval. The system of equations

$$x = f_1(t), \quad y = f_2(t), \quad z = f_3(t)$$

are called the *equations* of the curve γ in the parametric form.

A curve is defined uniquely by its equations in the parametric form. In this connection, then, we may speak about the definition of a curve by its equations.

§ 2. **Simple curve.** A set G of points in space is said to be *open* if for every point X of this set we can find a number $\epsilon > 0$ such that all the points in space whose distances from X are less than ϵ also belong to G. Obviously, a set consisting of an arbitrary number of open sets is open.

A *neighborhood* of the point X in space is any open set containing this point.

A set M of points in space is said to be connected if there do not exist two open sets G' and G'' which decompose the set M into two subsets M' and M'', one of which belongs only to G' and the other only to G''.

We shall now define a simple curve.

A set γ of points in space will be called a *simple curve* if this set is connected and each of its points X has a neighborhood N such that the part of γ lying in N is an elementary curve.

The structure of a simple curve *in the large* is clarified by the following theorem.

THEOREM. *The image of an open interval or circumference under a one-to-one and bicontinuous mapping into space is a simple curve.*

Conversely, a simple curve is the image of an open interval or circumference under a one-to-one and bicontinuous mapping into space. Briefly, this can be expressed as follows: a simple curve is homeomorphic to either an open interval or to a circumference.

We shall not set down the proof of this theorem. We shall only remark that the property of a simple curve of being homeomorphic

i.e., a connected 1-manifold is either ℝ or S¹.

to an open interval or a circumference, indicated in the theorem, completely characterizes the curve and, consequently, a simple curve can be defined by means of this property.

A simple curve which is homeomorphic to a circumference is said to be *closed*.

We shall define the concept of a neighborhood of a point on a simple curve.

A neighborhood of a point X on a simple curve γ is the common part of the curve γ and some neighborhood of the point X in space. According to the definition, each point of a simple curve has a neighborhood which is an elementary curve. In the sequel, when we talk about a neighborhood of a point on a curve, we shall have in mind such an elementary neighborhood.

Suppose a simple curve γ is the image of an open interval or a circumference g under a one-to-one and bicontinuous mapping f. Let X be an arbitrary point of g and let ω be any neighborhood of X. Then the image of ω under the mapping f is a neighborhood of the point $f(X)$ on the curve γ. Conversely, any neighborhood of the point $f(X)$ can be obtained in this manner.

The proof of this assertion is straightforward. The image of ω under the mapping f is an elementary curve, inasmuch as ω is an open interval or an open arc of a circumference, and f is one-to-one and bicontinuous.

In virtue of the bicontinuity of the mapping f, a sphere $\sigma(Y)$, which does not contain any other points of the curve γ except the points $f(\omega)$, can be described about each point $f(Y)$ belonging to $f(\omega)$. The set G consisting of all such open spheres $\sigma(Y)$ is open. This open set contains only those points of the curve γ which belong to the elementary curve $f(\omega)$. According to the definition, $f(\omega)$ is a neighborhood of the point $f(X)$ on the curve. This proves the first part of the assertion.

We shall now prove the second part. Suppose $f(\omega)$ is a neighborhood of the point $f(X)$ on the curve γ. Since $f(\omega)$ is an elementary curve, it is the image of an open interval $\alpha < \tau < \beta$ under a one-to-one and bicontinuous mapping φ. Suppose for definiteness that g is the open interval $a < t < b$. Each point τ is assigned a definite point on the curve γ, and to the latter point there corresponds a definite point t on the interval. Thus, t may be considered as a function of τ, $t = t(\tau)$.

The function $t(\tau)$ establishes a one-to-one and bicontinuous mapping of the open interval $\alpha < \tau < \beta$ onto the open interval $a < t < b$. The image of the interval $\alpha < \tau < \beta$ is the set ω.

We shall show that ω is an open interval. Because of the continuity of the function $t(\tau)$, if the points t' and t'' belong to the set ω then the closed interval $t' \le t \le t''$ also belongs to ω; this is so because a continuous function $t(\tau)$ which assumes the values t' and t'' also takes on all intermediate values. Thus, ω is an interval. We shall show that its endpoints do not belong to ω. In fact, a neighborhood of the point $f(X)$ on the curve γ is a part of the curve belonging to some open set G. If X belongs to ω, i.e. if the image of X belongs to G, then in virtue of the continuity of the mapping f the images of all points on the interval g which are sufficiently close to X also belong to G. It follows from this that ω is an open set and hence it is an open interval. This proves the second part of the assertion.

§ 3. General curve. A mapping f of a set M into space is said to be *locally one-to-one* if each of the points of M has a neighborhood in which the mapping f is one-to-one.

We now define a general curve.

A set γ of points in space will be called a *general curve* if this set is the image of a simple curve under a continuous and locally one-to-one mapping of it into space.

We shall say that the mapping f_1 of a simple curve γ_1 and the mapping f_2 of a simple curve γ_2 define one and the same general curve γ if a one-to-one and bicontinuous correspondence can be established between the points of the curves γ_1 and γ_2 where the images of corresponding points on these curves coincide on the curve γ.

In order to clarify the second part of the above definition, we shall introduce an example. A general curve is given in Fig. 1. This curve can be thought of as the image of a circumference under a one-to-one and continuous mapping in two distinct ways, which from the point of view of the given definition, yield distinct curves. Graphically, one may think of them as follows.

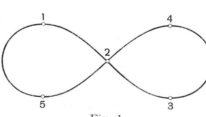

Fig. 1

Suppose a point moves on a circumference. Then its image moves along the curve. In this connection, the image-point, running along the curve, may assume successively the positions 1, 2, 3, 4, 2, 5, but it can also trace out the curve in the order 1, 2, 4, 3, 2, 5. Mappings, corresponding to these courses, define distinct general curves, although as point sets they coincide.

Suppose a general curve γ is the image under a one-to-one and bi-continuous mapping f of the simple curve $\bar{\gamma}$ into space. We shall say that a sequence of points $f(X_n)$ on the curve γ converges to the point $f(X)$, if the sequence of points X_n on the simple curve $\bar{\gamma}$ converges to the point X. A neighborhood of the point $f(X)$ on the curve γ is the image of any neighborhood of the point X on the curve $\bar{\gamma}$ under the mapping f.

Although convergent sequences of points on a general curve γ and neighborhoods of points on γ are defined as images of convergent sequences and neighborhoods on a simple curve under some definite mapping f, these concepts do not, however, depend on the particular character of the mapping f in the sense that, starting with another mapping f', another simple curve $\bar{\gamma}'$, defining the *same* general curve γ, we arrive at the same convergent sequences and the same neighborhoods of points on this curve.

This follows from the possibility of establishing a one-to-one and bicontinuous correspondence between the points of the simple curves $\bar{\gamma}$ and $\bar{\gamma}'$ where the images of corresponding points on these curves under the mappings f and f' coincide. The images of corresponding convergent sequences on the curves $\bar{\gamma}$ and $\bar{\gamma}'$ define the same convergent sequence on the curve γ. The images of corresponding neighborhoods of corresponding points on the curves $\bar{\gamma}$ and $\bar{\gamma}'$ define the same neighborhood of the point on the general curve.

If we consider a simple curve, in particular an elementary curve, as a general curve, then the concept of convergence of points on it is equivalent to the concept of geometric convergence, and the concept of neighborhood is equivalent to the concept of geometric neighborhood, introduced for simple curves.

Since a general curve is the image of a simple curve under a locally one-to-one and continuous mapping, and a simple curve is the image of an open interval or a circumference under a one-to-one and bicontinuous mapping, a general curve is the image of an open interval or a circumference under a locally one-to-one and continuous mapping. Such a mapping can be given analytically by means of the equations

$$x = f_1(t), \quad y = f_2(t), \quad z = f_3(t),$$

where f_1, f_2, f_3 are functions defined on the open interval $a < t < b$ or on the half-open interval $a \leq t < b$. This system of equations are called the equations of the curve in the parametric form.

§ 4. Regular curve. Analytic definition of a curve. It follows from the definition of a general curve that there exists a neighborhood for each of its points which is an elementary curve.

We shall say that the curve γ is *regular* (*k*-times differentiable) if each of the points of this curve has a neighborhood which permits a regular parametrization, i.e. the possibility of giving its equations in the parametric form

$$x = f_1(t), \quad y = f_2(t), \quad z = f_3(t),$$

where f_1, f_2, f_3 are regular (*k*-times continuously differentiable) functions. For $k = 1$, the curve is said to be *smooth*.

A curve is said to be *analytic* if it permits of an analytic parametrization (the functions f_1, f_2, f_3 are analytic) in a sufficiently small neighborhood of each of its points.

In the sequel we shall consider regular curves exclusively.

As was shown in the preceding section, a curve may be given by means of equations in the parametric form

$$x = x(t), \quad y = y(t), \quad z = z(t),$$

where $x(t)$, $y(t)$, $z(t)$ are certain functions defined in some open interval $a < t < b$ or half-open interval $a \leq t < b$.

The question naturally arises, when does the system of equations

$$x = x(t), \quad y = y(t), \quad z = z(t) \quad (a < t < b)$$

define a regular curve, i.e. when can these equations be considered as the equations of some curve? The answer to this question is given in many cases by the following theorem.

THEOREM. *If $x(t)$, $y(t)$ and $z(t)$ are regular functions, satisfying the condition*

$$x'^2(t) + y'^2(t) + z'^2(t) > 0 \quad (a < t < b),$$

then the system of equations

$$x = x(t), \quad y = y(t), \quad z = z(t) \quad (a < t < b)$$

are the equations of some curve γ. This curve is the image of the open interval $a < t < b$ under a continuous and locally one-to-one mapping which assigns to the point t on the open interval the point in space with coordinates $x(t)$, $y(t)$, $z(t)$.

Obviously, only the assertion about the local one-to-oneness of the indicated mapping is necessary in the proof. We shall prove this assertion.

If the assertion is not true, then there exists a t_0 in an arbitrarily small neighborhood of which we can find t_1 and t_2 ($t_1 \neq t_2$) such that

$$x(t_1) - x(t_2) = 0, \quad y(t_1) - y(t_2) = 0, \quad z(t_1) - z(t_2) = 0.$$

By the mean value theorem we obtain from this that

$$x'(\vartheta_1) = 0, \quad y'(\vartheta_2) = 0, \quad z'(\vartheta_3) = 0,$$

where ϑ_1, ϑ_2, ϑ_3 are between t_1 and t_2. Since t_1 and t_2 are arbitrarily close to t_0, by the continuity of the functions $x'(t)$, $y'(t)$, and $z'(t)$, we have

$$x'(t_0) = 0, \quad y'(t_0) = 0, \quad z'(t_0) = 0$$

and, consequently,

$$x'^2(t_0) + y'^2(t_0) + z'^2(t_0) = 0.$$

We have therefore arrived at a contradiction. This completes the proof of the assertion.

Some simple curves permit a parametrization of the form

$$x = t, \quad y = \varphi(t), \quad z = \psi(t) \quad (a < t < b)$$

for a suitable choice of the x, y, z coordinate axes. The equations of such a curve can be written in the equivalent form

$$y = \varphi(x), \quad z = \psi(x) \quad (a < x < b).$$

THEOREM. *Suppose γ is a regular curve and that*

$$x = f_1(t), \quad y = f_2(t), \quad z = f_3(t) \quad (a < t < b)$$

is its regular parametrization in a neighborhood of the point (x_0, y_0, z_0), corresponding to $t = t_0$. Suppose $f_1'(t) \neq 0$ at this point. Then in a

sufficiently small neighborhood of the point t_0 the curve γ can be de-
fined by means of the equations

$$y = \varphi(x), \quad z = \psi(x),$$

where φ and ψ are regular functions of x.

In fact, according to the implicit function theorem there exists a regular function $\chi(x)$, equal to t_0 for $x = x_0$ and satisfying the equation

$$x = f_1(\chi(x))$$

for all x near x_0. Differentiating this identity and evaluating for $x = x_0$ we find $1 = f_1'(t_0)\chi'(x_0)$. It follows that $\chi'(x_0) \neq 0$. Thus, the function $\chi(x)$ is monotonic in a neighborhood of x_0 and consequently, for sufficiently small δ the mapping of the open interval $x_0 - \delta < \ < x < x_0 + \delta$ onto the t-axis, defined by the equation $t = \chi(x)$, will be one-to-one and bicontinuous.

It follows from this that in the neighborhood $\chi(x_0 - \delta) < t < \ < \chi(x_0 + \delta)$ the curve γ can be defined by the equations

$$y = f_2(\chi(x)), \quad z = f_3(\chi(x)) \quad (x_0 - \delta < x < x_0 + \delta).$$

This completes the proof of the theorem.

§ 5. On the implicit representation of a curve. For simplicity of presentation, the proofs of the fundamental propositions of this section will be carried out for the case of plane curves.

The corresponding propositions for space curves will be stated without proof.

A curve is said to be a *plane* curve if all of its points lie in a plane. We shall assume that this plane is the x, y-plane.

We shall say that a plane curve is defined by the equation

$$\varphi(x, y) = 0,$$

expressing by this only the fact that the coordinates of points on the curve satisfy the given equation. In this connection, there may exist points in the plane which satisfy the given equation but do not belong to the curve.

Thus, defining a curve by means of the equation $\varphi(x, y) = 0$, in distinction to the parametric definition considered above, is incomplete. Nonetheless, some questions concerning the curve can be answered if we have even such an incomplete definition of it.

In the consideration of curves, defined by equations in the implicit form, an important role is played by the following theorem.

THEOREM 1. *Suppose $\varphi(x, y)$ is a regular function of the arguments x, y. Suppose M is the set of points in the x, y-plane satisfying the equation $\varphi(x, y) = 0$; let (x_0, y_0) be a point in this set at which $\varphi_x{}^2 + \varphi_y{}^2 \neq 0$. Then the point (x_0, y_0) has a neighborhood such that all the points of the set M belonging to it form a regular elementary curve.*

PROOF. Suppose, for definiteness, that $\varphi_y \neq 0$ at the point (x_0, y_0). By the implicit function theorem, there exist positive numbers δ and ϵ, and a regular function $\psi(x)$, defined in the interval $x_0 - \delta < < x < x_0 + \delta$, such that all the points $(x, \psi(x))$, $x_0 - \delta < x < x_0 + \delta$ satisfy the equation $\varphi(x, y) = 0$, where these points are the only points of the rectangle $x_0 - \delta < x < x_0 + \delta$, $y_0 - \epsilon < y < y_0 + \epsilon$ satisfying the equation $\varphi(x, y) = 0$. The elementary curve, about which we are talking in the theorem, is defined by means of the equation

$$y = \psi(x), \quad (x_0 - \delta < x < x_0 + \delta).$$

This proves the theorem.

The corresponding theorem for space curves consists in the following.

Suppose $\varphi(x, y, z)$ and $\psi(x, y, z)$ are regular functions of the arguments x, y, z. Suppose M is the set of points in space, satisfying the equations

$$\varphi(x, y, z) = 0, \quad \psi(x, y, z) = 0,$$

and (x_0, y_0, z_0) is a point in this set at which the rank of the matrix

$$\begin{pmatrix} \varphi_x & \varphi_y & \varphi_z \\ \psi_x & \psi_y & \psi_z \end{pmatrix}$$

equals two. Then the point (x_0, y_0, z_0) has a neighborhood such that all the points of the set M belonging to it form a regular elementary curve.

The proof of this theorem is also based on the application of the implicit function theorem and does not differ fundamentally from the proof of the corresponding theorem for plane curves.

§ 6. Singular points on regular plane curves. Suppose γ is a regular plane curve and P is a point on γ.

A point P on the curve γ is called a *regular point* if the curve permits a regular parametrization $x = x(t)$, $y = y(t)$ in a neighborhood of this point satisfying the condition $x'^2 + y'^2 \neq 0$ at the point P. But if such a parametrization does not exist, then P is called a *singular point* of the curve.

Thus, $x' = y' = 0$ at a singular point for an arbitrary regular parametrization of a regular curve.

We now consider in more detail the question of singular points on plane analytic curves.

LEMMA. *Suppose γ is an analytic curve and that O is a point on γ. Then with a suitable choice of coordinate axes the curve can be parametrized so that its equations will have the form*

$$x = a_1 t^{n_1},$$
$$y = b_1 t^{m_1} + b_2 t^{m_2} + \cdots, \quad n_1 \leq m_1$$

in a neighborhood of the point O.

PROOF. We take the point O as the origin of coordinates. Suppose $x = x(t)$, $y = y(t)$ is any analytic parametrization of the curve. Without loss of generality, we may assume that the point O corresponds to the value $t = 0$ of the parameter.

Suppose the first nonzero derivatives of the functions $x(t)$ and $y(t)$ at the point $t = 0$ have orders n_1 and m_1 respectively, where $n_1 \leq m_1$. (If $n_1 > m_1$, the roles of x and y can be interchanged.)

We introduce a new parameter s related to t by means of the equation

$$s = t \left(\frac{x(t)}{x^{n_1}(0) t^{n_1}} \right)^{1/n_1}.$$

For such a choice of the parameter, the equations of the curve γ have the form

$$x = \bar{a}_1 s^{n_1},$$
$$y = \bar{b}_1 s^{m_1} + \bar{b}_2 s^{m_2} + \cdots,$$

in a neighborhood of the point O, which was to be proved.

THEOREM. *Suppose an analytic curve is defined by means of the equations*

$$x = a_1 t^{n_1},$$
$$y = b_1 t^{m_1} + b_2 t^{m_2} + \cdots, \quad n_1 \leq m_1$$

in a neighborhood of the point O. Then a necessary and sufficient condition that the point O be a singular point on the curve is that at least one of the m_k not be divisible by n_1.

PROOF. *Necessity.* We note first of all that all the m_k and n_1 cannot be even, since then $x(t) = x(-t)$, $y(t) = y(-t)$ for arbitrarily small t, i.e. the one-to-oneness condition on the values of the mapping in an arbitrarily small neighborhood of the point $t = 0$ is invalidated.

Suppose all the m_k are multiples of n_1 (where n_1, obviously, is odd). We introduce the parameter $s = t^{n_1}$ to replace t. Then the equation of the curve in a neighborhood of the point O assumes the form

$$x = a_1 s,$$
$$y = b_1 s^{k_1} + b_2 s^{k_2} + \cdots.$$

Obviously, the point O corresponding to the value $s = 0$ of the parameter is a regular point on the curve.

Sufficiency. Suppose at least one of the m_k is not divisible by n_1. We shall show that the point O is a singular point. If the point O is a regular point, then in a neighborhood of O the curve can be defined by either the equation $y = \varphi(x)$ ($\varphi(x)$ is an analytic function) or by the equation $x = \psi(y)$ (where ψ is an analytic function).

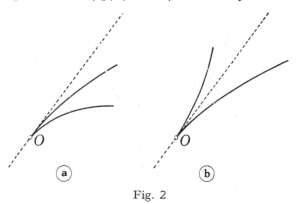

Fig. 2

Since y/x tends to a finite limit as $t \to 0$, the curve can indeed be defined by the equation

$$y = \varphi(x) = c_1 x + c_2 x^2 + \cdots$$

in a neighborhood of the point O. Substituting $x = x(t)$ and $y = y(t)$ into this equation, we obtain the identity

$$b_1 t^{m_1} + b_2 t^{m_2} + \cdots = c_1 a_1 t^{n_1} + c_2 a_1^2 t^{2n_1} + \cdots.$$

It follows from this that all the m_k are multiples of n_1. We have therefore arrived at a contradiction. This completes the proof of the theorem.

REMARK. If the point O is a singular point, where n_1 and m_1 are even, then it is called a *turning point of the second kind*. A curve has the form shown in Fig. 2*a* in a neighborhood of this point.

If the point O is singular, where m_1 is not divisible by n_1, and n_1 is even and m_1 is odd, then O is called a *turning point of the first kind*. The form of a curve in a neighborhood of such a singular point is shown in Fig. 2*b*.

We have seen that the answer to the question whether a point on a curve is a singular point or a regular point, is equivalent to investigating some special parametrization of the curve. In order to obtain this parametrization it is sufficient to know how to expand the functions $x(t)$ and $y(t)$ of an arbitrary analytic definition of the curve in a power series of analytic functions

$$ s = t\left(\frac{x(t)}{x^{n_1}(0)t^{n_1}}\right)^{1/n_1}. $$

The Bürman-Lagrange theorem known from the theory of analytic functions asserts that these expansions can be found.

In conclusion, we point out a simple sufficiency criterion that the point O on the curve γ be a singular point.

THEOREM. *Suppose the analytic curve γ is defined by means of the equations*

$$ x = x(t), \quad y = y(t) $$

where $x(t)$ and $y(t)$ are analytic functions of the parameter t in a neighborhood of the point O. Suppose the first nonzero derivatives of the functions $x(t)$ and $y(t)$ have orders n_1 and m_1 respectively, where $n_1 < m_1$.

Then the point O will be a singular point if m_1 is not divisible by n_1. Here, the point O will be a turning point of the second kind if both n_1 and m_1 are even, and a turning point of the first kind if n_1 is even and m_1 is odd.

§ 7. Singular points on analytic curves, defined by equations in the implicit form.

Suppose a plane analytic curve γ is defined by means of the equation $\varphi(x, y) = 0$, where $\varphi(x, y)$ is an analytic function of the variables x and y.

If $\varphi_x{}^2 + \varphi_y{}^2 \neq 0$ at the point $O(x_0, y_0)$ on the curve γ, then this point on the curve is a regular point as was shown in § 5. Thus, the only points on the curve which can be singular points are those at which $\varphi_x = \varphi_y = 0$.

Without loss of generality, we may assume that the point O is the origin of coordinates. In a neighborhood of the point O, the curve γ permits a parametrization of the form

$$x = a_1 t^{n_1},$$
$$y = b_1 t^{m_1} + b_2 t^{m_2} + \cdots,$$

where one may assume that $n_1 \leq m_1$. Otherwise, we can interchange the x and y axes. In order to determine whether the point O is a singular point of the curve and to explain the nature of the singularity at this point, it is sufficient to know the exponents n_1, m_1, m_2, $\cdots$.

In order to determine these exponents, we make use of the identity

$$\varphi(x(t), y(t)) \equiv 0.$$

The extent of this course does not permit us to stop to consider this question in more detail, and we shall restrict ourselves to the following remarks. The exponents n_1, m_1, m_2, $\cdots$ are not defined uniquely by the above identity. This is due not only to the fact that going over to a new variable s according to the formula $t = s^k$ does not change the character of the parametrization but also to the fact that in the general case several analytic curves which are geometrically different, even in an arbitrarily small neighborhood of the point O, will satisfy the equation $\varphi(x, y) = 0$. In this connection, the character of the singularity of the point O on various curves will be distinct. The investigation of the singular point O for a curve, defined by the equation $\varphi(x, y) = 0$, must be understood in the sense of investigating the nature of the singularity of the point O with respect to every analytic curve, defined in a neighborhood of the point O by means of the equation $\varphi(x, y) = 0$.

We shall now consider an example.

Suppose the expansion of the function $\varphi(x, y)$ in powers of x, y begins with terms of the second degree

$$\varphi(x, y) = a_{20}x^2 + a_{11}xy + a_{02}y^2 + \cdots.$$

We shall distinguish three cases:

a) $a_{20}a_{02} - \frac{1}{4}a_{11}{}^2 > 0$;   b) $a_{20}a_{02} - \frac{1}{4}a_{11}{}^2 < 0$;
c) $a_{20}a_{02} - \frac{1}{4}a_{11}{}^2 = 0$.

By means of a rotation of axes, we can attain the case where the term containing xy will be absent in the expansion of the function $\varphi(x, y)$ in a power series.

Substituting $x(t)$ and $y(t)$ into the expansion of the function $\varphi(x, y)$ we obtain an identity in t. For $n_1 < m_1$, the lowest power of t, equal to $2n_1$, has only one term, namely $a_{20}a_1{}^2t^{2n_1}$. It follows that $a_{20} = 0$, which is impossible either in the first or in the second case. It remains to assume that $n_1 = m_1$. Then in the first two cases, the terms $a_{20}a_1{}^2t^{2n_1}$ and $a_{02}b_1{}^2t^{2m_1}$ have the lowest degree. This is also impossible in the first case, since a_{20} and a_{02} have the same sign, and it follows from the identity that $a_{20}a_1{}^2 + a_{02}b_1{}^2 = 0$.

Thus, in the first case there does not exist an analytic curve which satisfies the equation $\varphi(x, y) = 0$ and contains the point O. It turns out, in this case, that in a sufficiently small neighborhood of the point O no points exist which are different from O and satisfy the equation $\varphi(x, y) = 0$. When the curve is defined as the geometric locus of points satisfying the equation $\varphi(x, y) = 0$, such a point is called an *isolated* singular point.

In the second case, we obtain two systems of values for a_1 and b_1, with accuracy up to within an unessential factor,

$$a_1 = \sqrt{|a_{02}|}, \quad b_1 = \sqrt{|a_{20}|};$$
$$a_1 = \sqrt{|a_{02}|}, \quad b_1 = -\sqrt{|a_{20}|}.$$

Now if we begin with any system of values for a_1 and b_1, and $n_1 = m_1$, then the exponents m_k and the coefficients b_k are already uniquely determined by the identity $\varphi(x(t), y(t)) \equiv 0$. It is not difficult to prove that all the exponents m_k are multiples of $n_1 = m_1$. Thus, in the second case there exist two analytic curves, geometrically distinct in an arbitrarily small neighborhood of the point O. The point O is a regular point for these curves inasmuch as all m_k are divisible by n_1. When the curve is defined as the geometric locus of points satisfying the equation $\varphi(x, y) = 0$, the point O is still considered as a singular point in the case under consideration, and it is called a *nodal* point.

Finally, we consider the third case. In this case we may assume that $a_{20} = 0$ since $a_{20}a_{02} = 0$. The expansion of the function $\varphi(x, y)$ has the form

$$\varphi(x, y) = a_{02}y^2 + a_{30}x^3 + \cdots.$$

We shall assume that $a_{30} \neq 0$. This corresponds in the general case to the fact that the forms $\varphi_2 = a_{20}x^2 + a_{11}xy + a_{02}y^2$ and $\varphi_3 = a_{30}x^3 + \cdots + a_{03}y^3$ do not have common divisors.

Substituting $x(t)$ and $y(t)$ for x and y in the expansion of the function $\varphi(x, y)$, we note that the terms with the lowest powers of t are $a_{02}b_1^2t^{2m_1}$ and $a_{30}a_1^3t^{3n_1}$. It follows from this that $2m_1 = 3n_1$, i.e. m_1 is not divisible by n_1. Consequently, the point O is a singular point of the curve.

It turns out that if both m_1 and n_1 are assumed to be even, then all the m_k turn out to be even, since they can be expressed linearly and homogeneously in terms of m_1 and n_1. But, as was noted above, n_1 and all the m_k cannot be even. Therefore, only n_1 is even. This means that the singular point O is a turning point of the first kind.

§ 8. **Asymptotes to curves.** Suppose γ is a non-closed curve and that

$$x = x(t), \quad y = y(t) \quad (a < t < b)$$

are its equations. We say that a curve tends to infinity from one side if $x^2(t) + y^2(t) \to \infty$ as $t \to a$ (or as $t \to b$). But if $x^2(t) + y^2(t) \to \infty$ for both $t \to a$ and $t \to b$, we say the curve tends to infinity from both sides. Obviously, the property of a curve to tend to infinity does not depend on its parametrization.

Suppose the curve γ tends to infinity, for example, $x^2 + y^2 \to \infty$ as $t \to a$. The straight line g is called an *asymptote* to the curve γ if the distance $d(t)$ of a point on the curve γ to the straight line g tends to zero when $t \to a$.

THEOREM. *A necessary and sufficient condition that the curve γ defined by the equations*

$$x = x(t), \quad y = y(t) \quad (a < t < b)$$

and tending to infinity as $t \to a$, have an asymptote is that

1. *Each of the two ratios*

$$x(t)/\rho(t), \quad y(t)/\rho(t), \quad \text{where } \rho(t) = \{x^2(t) + y^2(t)\}^{\frac{1}{2}},$$

tend to a limit. Suppose, for definiteness, that

$$x(t)/\rho(t) \to \alpha, \quad y(t)/\rho(t) \to \beta;$$

2. *The expression*

$$- \beta x(t) + \alpha y(t)$$

also tends to a definite limit as $t \to a$, provide the first condition is satisfied.

If this limit is denoted by p, then the equation of the asymptote will be

$$- \beta x + \alpha y - p = 0.$$

PROOF. Suppose g is an asymptote to the curve and that α and β are its direction cosines. The equation of the straight line can be written in the form

$$- \beta x + \alpha y - p = 0.$$

The point $Q(t)$ on the curve tends to infinity, coming arbitrarily close to the straight line g as $t \to a$. It follows from this that the ratios $x(t)/\rho(t)$, $y(t)/\rho(t)$ as $t \to a$ converge either to α and β, or to $- \alpha$ and $- \beta$, depending on which of the two directions on the straight line g the projection of the point $Q(t)$ tends to infinity. Suppose, for definiteness, that

$$x(t)/\rho(t) \to \alpha, \quad y(t)/\rho(t) \to \beta.$$

The quantity $- \beta x(t) + \alpha y(t) - p$ is equal, to within sign, to the distance from the point $Q(t)$ to the straight line g and, consequently, it tends to zero. Therefore, the expression $- \beta x(t) + \alpha y(t)$ tends to a definite limit (p) as $t \to a$. This completes the proof of the necessity portion of the theorem.

We shall now prove the sufficiency. Suppose

$$x(t)/\rho(t) \to \alpha, \quad y(t)/\rho(t) \to \beta, \quad \alpha y(t) - \beta x(t) \to p$$

as $t \to a$. We shall show that the straight line g with equation

$$- \beta x + \alpha y - p = 0$$

is an asymptote to the curve. In fact, the expression

$$- \beta x(t) + \alpha y(t) - p$$

is, to within sign, the distance from the point t on the curve to the straight line g. But

$$- \beta x(t) + \alpha y(t) + p \to 0$$

as $t \to a$.

This completes the proof of the theorem.

EXAMPLE. Suppose the curve γ is defined by the equation

$$y = \varphi(x) \quad (a < x < b)$$

or, what amounts to the same thing,

$$x = t, \quad y = \varphi(t) \quad (a < t < b).$$

Suppose $\varphi(t) \to \infty$ as $t \to a$.

When $t \to a$,

$$\frac{t}{\sqrt{t^2 + \varphi^2(t)}} \to 0, \qquad \frac{\varphi(t)}{\sqrt{t^2 + \varphi^2(t)}} \to 1,$$

$$-t + 0 \cdot \varphi(t) \to -a.$$

Thus, as $t \to a$, we see that the curve has the asymptote

$$x - a = 0.$$

We now consider the problem of asymptotes to a curve defined by means of an equation in the implicit form $\varphi(x, y) = 0$.

As noted, the equation $\varphi(x, y) = 0$ defines a curve only in the sense that points on the curve satisfy the equation $\varphi(x, y) = 0$ but, generally speaking, these do not exhaust all points in the plane which have this property. The problem of finding the asymptotes to a curve, defined by means of the equation $\varphi(x, y) = 0$, is not completely defined. It turns out to be possible to only point out some set of lines which contain the asymptotes among them.

We shall restrict ourselves to the case of algebraic curves (i.e. the case where $\varphi(x, y)$ is a polynomial in the variables x and y).

Suppose

$$x = \bar{x} + \lambda u,$$

$$y = \bar{y} + \mu u$$

are the equations of the asymptote in the parametric form. Suppose $Q(u)$ is a point on the curve which is the closest to the point u on the asymptote. The coordinates of the point Q are

$$x(u) = \bar{x} + \lambda u + \xi(u),$$

$$y(u) = \bar{y} + \mu u + \eta(u),$$

where

$$\xi(u) \text{ and } \eta(u) \to 0 \text{ as } u \to \infty.$$

We denote by φ_k the set of all terms of degree k in the polynomial φ. We shall then have

$$\varphi = \varphi_n + \varphi_{n-1} + \cdots + \varphi_0.$$

Substituting $x = x(u)$, $y = y(u)$ for x, y in $\varphi(x, y)$ and factoring terms containing u^n and u^{n-1}, we obtain

$$\varphi(x(u), y(u)) = u^n \varphi_n(\lambda, \mu) +$$
$$u^{n-1}\{\bar{x}(\varphi_n(\lambda, \mu))_\lambda' + \bar{y}(\varphi_n(\lambda, \mu))_\mu' + \varphi_{n-1}(\lambda, \mu)\} + \cdots.$$

In the right member of this equation, terms having powers less than u^{n-1} are not written out.

Since $\varphi(x(u), y(u)) \equiv 0$ and, consequently, $\dfrac{1}{u^n} \varphi(x(u), y(u)) \to 0$ as $u \to \infty$, we have $\varphi_n(\lambda, \mu) = 0$.

In an analogous manner, we obtain

$$\bar{x}(\varphi_n(\lambda, \mu))_\lambda' + \bar{y}(\varphi_n(\lambda, \mu))_\mu' + \varphi_{n-1}(\lambda, \mu) = 0.$$

Since (x, y) is any point on the asymptote, this equation is the equation of the asymptote.

EXERCISES FOR CHAPTER I

1. A point M moves in space in such a way that its projection onto the x, y-plane moves uniformly along the circumference $x^2 + y^2 = a^2$ with angular velocity ω, and its projection onto the z-axis moves uniformly with velocity c. The curve traced out by the point M is called a simple helix. Derive the equation of the helix in the parametric form taking time t as the parameter. Assume that the coordinates of the point M are $(a, 0, 0)$ at the initial moment $(t = 0)$.

ANSWER: $x = a \cos \omega t$, $y = a \sin \omega t$, $z = ct$.

2. A simple helix (see Exercise 1) is projected onto the x, y-plane by means of parallel straight lines which form an angle ϑ with the z-axis. Find the equation of the projection. For what ϑ will the projection have singular points? Discuss the nature of the singular points.

ANSWER: If the projecting lines are parallel to the y, z-plane, then the equations of the projection will be

$$x = a \cos \omega t, \quad y = ct \tan \vartheta + a \sin \omega t.$$

The projection will have singular points if $\tan \vartheta = a\omega/c$. The singular points are turning points of the first kind.

3. A circular disc of radius a rolls uniformly without slipping along the straight line g with velocity v. Find the equation of the curve γ which is described by a point M which is fixed to the circular disc. Under what condition does the curve have singular points? Discuss the nature of the singular points.

ANSWER: If the straight line g is taken to be the x-axis and the point M is initially on the y-axis below the center of the circular disc, then the equations of the curve γ will be

$$x = vt - b \sin vt/a, \quad y = a - b \cos vt/a,$$

where b is the distance of the point M from the center of the circular disc. The curve has singular points if the point M is on the circumference of the circular disc (in this case the curve γ is called a *cycloid*). Singular points are turning points of the first kind.

4. Investigate the singular points of the semicubical parabola $y^2 = x^3$.

ANSWER: $(0, 0)$ is a singular point; it is a turning point of the first kind.

5. Prove that a curve defined by means of the equation

$$|x|^{2/3} + |y|^{2/3} = a^{2/3} \text{ (astroid)}$$

is an analytic curve. Find its singular points. Discuss the nature of the singular points.

ANSWER: The curve obviously permits the analytic parametrization

$$x = a \cos^3 t, \quad y = a \sin^3 t,$$

and consequently, it is analytic. The singular points are $(0, 1)$, $(0, -1)$, $(1, 0)$, $(-1, 0)$. The singular points are turning points of the first kind.

6. Write down the equations of the asymptotes to the following curves:

a) $x = a \sin t$
   $y = a(\cos t + \ln \tan t/2)$ (tractrix);
b) $x^3 + y^3 - 3axy = 0$ (folium of Descartes).

ANSWER:

a) $x = 0$.
b) $x + y + a = 0$.

PROBLEMS AND THEOREMS FOR CHAPTER I

1_1. Suppose the elementary curves γ_1 and γ_2 have a point in common and are subsets of a simple curve γ. Prove that at least one of the following properties holds:

a) the curves γ_1 and γ_2 form an elementary curve;

b) the curves γ_1 and γ_2 form the entire curve γ.

1_2. Prove that any simple curve can be covered with a finite or denumerable set of elementary curves.

1_3. Prove the theorem in § 2, Chapter I: Every simple curve is the image of an open segment or of a circumference under a one-to-one continuous mapping into space.

2. Suppose

$$x = x(t), \quad y = y(t), \quad z = z(t)$$

is any parametrization of an elementary curve. Then any other parametrization has the form

$$x = x(\sigma(\tau)), \quad y = y(\sigma(\tau)), \quad z = z(\sigma(\tau)),$$

where $\sigma(\tau)$ is a continuous strictly monotonic function.

3. What is the order of regularity of the curve defined by an equation in the implicit form $\varphi(x, y) = 0$ guaranteed by an n-times differentiable function if $\varphi_x^2 + \varphi_y^2 \neq 0$? Can the curve possess a higher order of regularity? Construct an example.

4. Construct an example of a curve which does not permit a smooth parametrization of any subset of itself.

5. Suppose a plane analytic curve γ is defined by the equation $\varphi(x, y) = 0$ in a neighborhood of the point (x_0, y_0) where φ is an analytic function. Suppose the function φ and all its derivatives up to and including that of the $(n - 1)$-st order vanish at the point (x_0, y_0). Prove that if all the zeros of the polynomial

$$P(\xi) = \Sigma_{k+l=n} \, \xi^k \, \frac{\partial^n \varphi}{\partial x^k \partial y^l} \Big|_{(x_0, \, y_0)}$$

are real and distinct, then the point (x_0, y_0) on the curve γ is a regular point in the sense of the definition in § 3, Chapter I.

6. Find the conditions for the existence of an asymptote to the space curve

$$x = x(t), \quad y = y(t), \quad z = z(t),$$

which tends to infinity as $t \to a$, analogous to that obtained in § 8, Chapter I, for a plane curve.

Write the equation of the asymptote.

7. Write the equation of the asymptotes to an algebraic space curve, defined by means of the equations, in the implicit form,

$$\varphi(x, y, z) = 0, \quad \psi(x, y, z) = 0,$$

where φ and ψ are polynomials in x, y, and z, similar to the way this was done for plane curves in § 8, Chapter I.

CHAPTER II

CONCEPTS FOR CURVES WHICH ARE RELATED TO THE CONCEPT OF CONTACT

Suppose M and $\bar{M}$ are sets of points in space having the point O in common. Let X be an arbitrary point in the set $\bar{M}$, $h(X)$ its distance from the set M (the greatest lower bound of the distances of the points of the set M from the point X) and $d(X)$ the distance of the point X from the point O.

We shall say that the set $\bar{M}$ has contact with the set M in the point O if the ratio $h(X)/d^{\alpha}(X)$ ($\alpha \geq 1$) tends to zero when the point X approaches O arbitrarily closely. We shall introduce many concepts for curves using the notion of contact. We shall consider these concepts in the present chapter.

§ 1. Vector functions of a scalar argument. In the following discussion we shall make extensive use of the methods of vector analysis. In this connection, we first recall the definition of certain concepts.

Suppose G is an arbitrary set of points on the real line, in a plane or in space. We say that a vector function f is defined on the set G is f assigns a vector $f(X)$ to each point X in G.

The concept of limit is introduced for vector functions the way this is done in analysis for scalar functions. We say that $f(X) \to a$ as $X \to X_0$ if $|f(X) - a| \to 0$ when $X \to X_0$.

Theorems on limits, analogous to limit theorems for scalar functions, hold for vector functions. For example, if $f(X)$ and $g(X)$ are vector functions and $\lambda(X)$ is a scalar function for which $f(X) \to a$, $g(X) \to b$ and $\lambda(X) \to m$ as $X \to X_0$ then

$$f(X) \pm g(X) \to a \pm b,$$
$$\lambda(X)f(X) \to ma,$$
$$f(X) \cdot g(X) \to a \cdot b,$$
$$f(X) \times g(X) \to a \times b.$$

The proof of these assertions does not differ fundamentally from the proof of the corresponding assertions for scalar functions in analysis. For example, we shall prove the last assertion. We have

$$|f(X) \times g(X) - a \times b| = |f(X) \times (g(X) - b) - b \times (f(X) - a)| \leq$$
$$|f(X) \times (g(X) - b)| + |b \times (f(X) - a)| \leq$$
$$|f(X)| \, |g(X) - b| + |b| \, |f(X) - a|.$$

It follows from this that $|f(X) \times g(X) - a \times b| \to 0$ as $X \to X_0$. And this means that $f(X) \times g(X) \to a \times b$.

The concept of continuity for a vector function is introduced the same way it is done for scalar functions. Namely, the function $f(X)$ is said to be continuous at the point X_0 if $f(X) \to f(X_0)$ as $X \to X_0$.

Suppose $f(X)$ and $g(X)$ are vector functions which are continuous at the point X_0, and that $\lambda(X)$ is a scalar function which is continuous at this point. Then the vector functions

$$\lambda(X)f(X), \; f(X) \pm g(X), \; f(X) \times g(X),$$

and also the scalar function $f(X) \cdot g(X)$ are continuous at the point X_0. This continuity property is a simple consequence of properties of the limit.

We now discuss the concept of derivative.

Suppose $f(t)$ is a vector function defined on a closed interval. We say that the vector function f has a derivative at the point t on an open interval if the limit of the ratio

$$\frac{f(t + h) - f(t)}{h}$$

exists as $h \to 0$. We denote the derivative of $f(t)$ at the point t by $f'(t)$.

If $f(t)$ and $g(t)$ are vector functions which are differentiable functions at the point t, and $\lambda(t)$ is a scalar function, differentiable at this point, then $\lambda(t)f(t), \; f(t) \pm g(t), \; f(t) \times g(t), \; f(t) \cdot g(t)$ are functions which are differentiable at t and we have

$$(\lambda f)' = \lambda' f + \lambda f',$$
$$(f \pm g)' = f' \pm g',$$
$$(f \times g)' = f' \times g + f \times g',$$
$$(f \cdot g)' = f' \cdot g + f \cdot g'.$$

These differentiation formulas are obtained exactly as the corresponding formulas for the differentiation of scalar functions in analysis.

The derivative of the vector function $f'(t)$ is called the second derivative of the function $f(t)$ and is denoted by $f''(t)$. The third, fourth, fifth, and higher derivatives are defined analogously. A function, having continuous derivatives up to the k-th order inclusively, on the open interval (a, b), is called a k-times differentiable function on this open interval.

Suppose e_1, e_2, e_3 are three vectors, not lying in one plane. Every vector r permits a representation of the form

$$r = x_1 e_1 + y e_2 + z e_3;$$

the numbers x, y, z are uniquely defined and are called the coordinates of the vector r with respect to the basis e_1, e_2, e_3. Suppose $r(t)$ is a vector function defined on a segment. We shall define three scalar functions $x(t)$, $y(t)$, $z(t)$ by the condition

$$r(t) = x(t)e_1 + y(t)e_2 + z(t)e_3.$$

Hence, if the functions $x(t)$, $y(t)$, $z(t)$ are continuous or differentiable, then the vector function $r(t)$ is continuous respectively differentiable. Conversely, if the vector function $r(t)$ is continuous or differentiable, then the functions $x(t)$, $y(t)$, $z(t)$ are continuous respectively differentiable.

In order to prove the second assertion, we form the scalar product of the equation $r(t) = x(t)e_1 + y(t)e_2 + z(t)e_3$ with the vector e_1', which is perpendicular to the vectors e_2 and e_3. We then obtain $x(t)(e_1 \cdot e_1') = r(t) \cdot e_1'$. From this it is clear that the continuity or the differentiability of the vector function $r(t)$ implies the continuity respectively the differentiability of the function $x(t)$. We proceed analogously for the functions $y(t)$ and $z(t)$.

The Taylor formula holds for vector functions. Namely, if $f(t)$ is an n-times differentiable function, then

$$f(t + \Delta t) = f(t) + \Delta t f'(t) + \cdots + \frac{\Delta t^n}{n!}(f^{(n)}(t) + \varepsilon(t, \Delta t)),$$

where $|\varepsilon(t, \Delta t)| \to 0$ as $\Delta t \to 0$.

In fact, $f(t) = x(t)e_1 + y(t)e_2 + z(t)e_3$. But

$$x(t + \Delta t) = x(t) + \Delta t x'(t) + \cdots + \frac{\Delta t^n}{n!}(x^{(n)}(t) + \varepsilon_1),$$

$$y(t + \Delta t) = y(t) + \Delta t y'(t) + \cdots + \frac{\Delta t^n}{n!}(y^{(n)}(t) + \varepsilon_2),$$

$$z(t + \Delta t) = z(t) + \Delta t z'(t) + \cdots + \frac{\Delta t^n}{n!}(z^{(n)}(t) + \varepsilon_3).$$

Multiplying these equations by e_1, e_2, e_3 respectively, adding, and then noting that $x^{(k)}e_1 + y^{k)}(t)e_2 + z^{(k)}(t)e_3 = f^{(k)}(t)$, we obtain the Taylor formula for the vector function $f(t)$.

The concept of integral in the Riemann sense for vector functions is introduced literally as in the case of scalar functions. The integral of a vector function possesses the usual properties. Namely, if $f(t)$ is a vector function which is continuous on the closed interval $a \leq t \leq b$, and $a < c < b$, then

$$\int_a^b f(t)dt = \int_a^c f(t)dt + \int_c^b f(t)dt.$$

If m is a constant, then

$$\int_a^b mf(t)dt = m \int_a^b f(t)dt.$$

If r is a constant vector then

$$\int_a^b r \cdot f(t)dt = r \cdot \int_a^b f(t)dt,$$

$$\int_a^b r \times f(t)dt = r \times \int_a^b f(t)dt.$$

The formula

$$\frac{d}{dx}\int_a^x f(t)dt = f(x)$$

for the differentiation of a definite integral is valid.

In conclusion, we note that the parametric definition of a curve by means of the equations

$$x = x(t), \quad y = y(t), \quad z = z(t)$$

is equivalent to the definition of the curve by means of one vector equation

$$r = r(t) = x(t)e_1 + y(t)e_2 + z(t)e_3,$$

where e_1, e_2, e_3 are unit vectors having the directions of the coordinate axes x, y, z.

§ 2. Tangent to a curve. Let γ be a curve, P a point on γ and let g be a straight line passing through the point P. Let us take a point Q on the curve and denote its distance from the point P and from the line g by d and h respectively (Fig. 3).

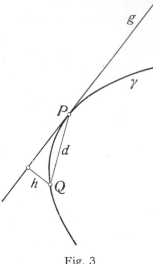

We shall call the line g the *tangent* to the curve γ at the point P if $h/d \to 0$ when $Q \to P$.

If the curve γ has a tangent at the point P then the straight line PQ approaches this tangent as $Q \to P$. Conversely, if the straight line PQ approaches some line g as $Q \to P$ then this straight line is a tangent. To prove this assertion it is sufficient to note that h/d

Fig. 3

is the sine of the angle between the lines g and PQ.

THEOREM. *A smooth curve γ has a unique tangent at each point. If $r = r(t)$ is the vector equation of the curve, then the tangent at the point P corresponding to the value t of the parameter, has the direction of the vector $r'(t)$.*

PROOF. Let us assume that the curve has a tangent g at the point P corresponding to the value t of the parameter. Suppose τ is a unit vector having the same direction as the line g. The distance d of the point Q, corresponding to the value $t + \Delta t$ of the parameter, from the point P is equal to $|r(t + \Delta t) - r(t)|$. The distance h of the point Q from the tangent equals $|(r(t + \Delta t) - r(t)) \times \tau|$. According to the definition of the tangent

$$\frac{h}{d} = \frac{|(r(t + \Delta t) - r(t)) \times \tau|}{|r(t + \Delta t) - r(t)|} \to 0 \text{ as } \Delta r \to 0.$$

But

$$\frac{|(r(t + \Delta t) - r(t)) \times \tau|}{|r(t + \Delta t) - r(t)|} = \frac{\left| \dfrac{r(t + \Delta t) - r(t)}{\Delta t} \times \tau \right|}{\left| \dfrac{r(t + \Delta t) - r(t)}{\Delta t} \right|} \to \frac{|r'(t) \times \tau|}{|r'(t)|}.$$

From this it follows that

$$r'(t) \times \tau = 0.$$

This is possible only when the vector τ has the same direction as the vector $r'(t)$. Thus, if the tangent exists, then it has the direction of the vector $r'(t)$ and, consequently, it is unique.

The fact that the line g, passing through the point P and having the same direction as the vector $r'(t)$, is a tangent, is also true; for, as the preceding discussions show, for such a line we have

$$\frac{h}{d} = \frac{\left| (r(t + \varDelta t) - r(t)) \times \dfrac{r'(t)}{|r'(t)|} \right|}{|r(t + \varDelta t) - r(t)|} \to \frac{|r'(t) \times r'(t)|}{|r'(t)|^2} = 0.$$

This completes the proof of the theorem.

Knowing the direction of the tangent, it is not difficult to write its equation. In fact, if the curve is given by means of the vector equation $r = r(t)$, then the position vector $\tilde{r}$ of an arbitrary point on the tangent can be represented in the form

$$\tilde{r} = r(t) + \lambda r'(t).$$

This is then the equation of the tangent in the parametric form (with parameter λ).

We shall write the equation of the tangent for a number of curves given in the analytic form.

Suppose the curve is given by means of equations in the parametric form

$$x = x(t), \quad y = y(t), \quad z = z(t).$$

Giving the curve in this form is equivalent to giving its equation in the vector form

$$r = r(t) = x(t)e_1 + y(t)e_2 + z(t)e_3,$$

where e_1, e_2, e_3 are unit vectors in the directions of the coordinate axes. Replacing the vector equation

$$\tilde{r} = r(t) + \lambda r'(t)$$

by three scalar equations, we obtain the equations of the tangent, corresponding to the parametric form

$$\tilde{x} = x(t) + \lambda x'(t), \quad \tilde{y} = y(t) + \lambda y'(t), \quad z = z(t) + \lambda z'(t)$$

or in the equivalent form

$$\frac{\tilde{x} - x(t)}{x'(t)} = \frac{\tilde{y} - y(t)}{y'(t)} = \frac{\tilde{z} - z(t)}{z'(t)}.$$

In the particular case of a plane curve given by means of the equations

$$x = x(t), \quad y = y(t),$$

the equation of its tangent is

$$\frac{\tilde{x} - x(t)}{x'(t)} = \frac{\tilde{y} - y(t)}{y'(t)}.$$

The equation of the tangent in the case when the curve is given by means of the equations

(*) $$y = y(x), \quad z = z(x)$$

is easily gotten from the equation of the tangent for the case where the curve is given in the parametric form. It suffices to note that giving the curve by means of the equations (*) is equivalent to giving it in the parametric form

$$x = t, \quad y = y(t), \quad z = z(t).$$

The equation of the tangent to the curve, given by means of the equations (*), is written as

$$\tilde{x} - x = \frac{\tilde{y} - y(x)}{y'(x)} = \frac{\tilde{z} - z(x)}{z'(x)}$$

or in the equivalent form

$$\tilde{y} = y(x) + y'(x)(\tilde{x} - x),$$
$$\tilde{z} = z(x) + z'(x)(\tilde{x} - x).$$

In particular, if we are dealing with a plane curve and its equation is $y = y(x)$, then the equation of the tangent to it will be

$$\tilde{y} = y(x) + y'(x)(\tilde{x} - x).$$

Finally, we write down the equation of the tangent at the point (x_0, y_0, z_0) to a curve given by the equations

$$\varphi(x, y, z) = 0, \quad \psi(x, y, z) = 0,$$

where the rank of the matrix

$$\begin{pmatrix} \varphi_x & \varphi_y & \varphi_z \\ \psi_x & \psi_y & \psi_z \end{pmatrix}$$

equals two. Suppose

$$x = x(t), \quad y = y(t), \quad z = z(t)$$

is any regular parametrization of the curve in a neighborhood of the point (x_0, y_0, z_0).

The equation of the tangent to the curve at the point (x_0, y_0, z_0) is

$$\frac{\tilde{x} - x_0}{x_0'} = \frac{\tilde{y} - y_0}{y_0'} = \frac{\tilde{z} - z_0}{z_0'}.$$

Thus, in order to obtain the equation of the tangent it suffices to know $x_0' : y_0' : z_0'$. We shall now compute these ratios.

We have the identities $\varphi(x(t), y(t), z(t)) \equiv 0$, $\psi(x(t), y(t), z(t)) \equiv 0$. Differentiating these identities with respect to t, we have

$$\varphi_x x' + \varphi_y y' + \varphi_z z' = 0,$$
$$\psi_x x' + \psi_y y' + \psi_z z' = 0.$$

It follows that

$$\frac{x'}{\begin{vmatrix} \varphi_y & \varphi_z \\ \psi_y & \psi_z \end{vmatrix}} = \frac{y'}{\begin{vmatrix} \varphi_z & \varphi_x \\ \psi_z & \psi_x \end{vmatrix}} = \frac{z'}{\begin{vmatrix} \varphi_x & \varphi_y \\ \psi_x & \psi_y \end{vmatrix}}$$

and the equation of the tangent assumes the form

$$\frac{\tilde{x} - x_0}{\begin{vmatrix} \varphi_y & \varphi_z \\ \psi_y & \psi_z \end{vmatrix}} = \frac{\tilde{y} - y_0}{\begin{vmatrix} \varphi_z & \varphi_x \\ \psi_z & \psi_x \end{vmatrix}} = \frac{\tilde{z} - z_0}{\begin{vmatrix} \varphi_x & \varphi_y \\ \psi_x & \psi_y \end{vmatrix}},$$

where the derivatives $\varphi_x, \varphi_y, \cdots, \psi_z$ are evaluated at the point of tangency (x_0, y_0, z_0).

If the curve lies in a plane and is defined by the equation $\varphi(x, y) = 0$, the equation of the tangent will be

$$\frac{\tilde{x} - x_0}{\varphi_x} = \frac{\tilde{y} - y_0}{\varphi_y}.$$

In order to derive this equation it is sufficient to note that defining a curve in the x, y-plane by the equation $\varphi(x, y) = 0$ is equivalent to defining it in space by means of the equations

$$\varphi(x, y) = 0, \quad z = 0.$$

The *normal* plane to a curve at the point P is the plane which passes through the point P and is perpendicular to the tangent at this point. Writing down the equation of this plane provided we know the equation of the tangent in case the curve is defined analytically does not present any difficulty and is left to the reader as an easy exercise.

§ 3. The osculating plane to a curve. Suppose γ is a curve and that P is a point on γ, and suppose α is a plane passing through the point P. We denote the distance of an arbitrary point Q on the curve from the plane α by h and the distance of this point from the point P by d (see Fig. 4).

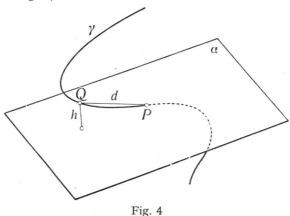

Fig. 4

We shall call the plane α the *osculating plane* to the curve γ at the point P if the ratio $h/d^2 \to 0$ when $Q \to P$.

THEOREM. *A regular (at least twice continuously differentiable) curve γ has an osculating plane at every point. In this connection, the osculating plane is either unique or any plane containing the tangent to the curve is an osculating plane. If $r = r(t)$ is the equation of the curve γ then the osculating plane at the point corresponding to the value t of the parameter, is parallel to the vectors $r'(t)$ and $r''(t)$.*

PROOF. Suppose α is an osculating plane to the curve γ at the point P, corresponding to the value t of the parameter. We shall denote the unit normal vector to the plane α by e. The distance of the point Q, corresponding to the value $t + \Delta t$ of the parameter, from the plane α is

$$h = |e \cdot (r(t + \Delta t) - r(t))|.$$

The distance from this point to P is

$$d = |r(t + \Delta t) - r(t)|.$$

We have

$$h/d^2 = \frac{|e \cdot (r(t + \Delta t) - r(t))|}{(r(t + \Delta t) - r(t))^2} = \frac{\left| e \cdot \left(r'(t)\Delta t + \dfrac{r''(t)}{2} \Delta t^2 + \varepsilon_1 \Delta t^2 \right) \right|}{(r'(t)\Delta t + \varepsilon_2 \Delta t)^2} =$$

$$= \frac{\left| \dfrac{e \cdot r'(t)}{\Delta t} + \dfrac{e \cdot r''(t)}{2} + \varepsilon_1' \right|}{r'^2(t) + \varepsilon_2'}.$$

Since $h/d^2 \to 0$, ε_1', $\varepsilon_2' \to 0$ as $\Delta t \to 0$, and $|r'(t)| \neq 0$, we have $e \cdot r'(t) = 0$, $e \cdot r''(t) = 0$. Thus, if the osculating plane exists, the vectors $r'(t)$ and $r''(t)$ are parallel to it.

It is not difficult to verify the fact that the osculating plane always exists. To this end, we take the plane α, parallel to the vectors $r'(t)$ and $r''(t)$ (we consider any plane to be parallel to the zero vector). Then $e \cdot r'(t) = e \cdot r''(t) = 0$ and, consequently, $h/d^2 = \dfrac{|\varepsilon_1'|}{r'^2(t) + \varepsilon_2'}$, as $\Delta t \to 0$.

Thus, the osculating plane exists at every point on the curve. Obviously, the osculating plane, being parallel to the vectors $r'(t)$ and $r''(t)$, will be unique if the vectors $r'(t)$ and $r''(t)$ are not parallel. But if these vectors are parallel (or the vector $r''(t) = 0$), then any plane, drawn through the tangent to the curve, will be an osculating plane.

We note that the osculating plane was defined purely geometrically, without recourse to any definite method of analytic definition. Therefore, the fact that the vectors r' and r'' are parallel expresses some geometric property of the curve.

We shall now derive the equation of the osculating plane. Suppose $r = r(t)$ is the vector equation of the curve and that t is the value of the parameter which corresponds to the point P on the curve. Suppose $r'(t)$ and $r''(t)$ are vectors which are not parallel at the point P. Then $r'(t) \times r''(t)$ will be the normal vector to the osculating plane. If $\tilde{r}$ denotes the position vector of any point in the osculating plane at the point P, then the vectors $\tilde{r} - r(t)$ and $r'(t) \times r''(t)$ are orthogonal. It follows that the equation of the osculating plane is

$$(\tilde{r} - r(t)) \cdot (r'(t) \times r''(t)) = 0$$

or

$$(\tilde{r} - r(t), r'(t), r''(t)) = 0.$$

In the case when the curve is defined parametrically

$$x = x(t), \quad y = y(t), \quad z = z(t),$$

we obtain from this equation the equation of the osculating plane in the form

$$\begin{vmatrix} \tilde{x} - x(t), & \tilde{y} - y(t), & \tilde{z} - z(t) \\ x'(t) & y'(t) & z'(t) \\ x''(t) & y''(t) & z''(t) \end{vmatrix} = 0.$$

The derivation of the equation of the osculating plane when the curve is defined analytically in other forms is left to the reader.

Every straight line passing through a point on the curve perpendicular to the tangent is called a *normal* to the curve. When the osculating plane is unique, two special straight lines are chosen from among these lines; they are the *principal normal* which is the normal lying in the osculating plane and the *binormal* which is the normal perpendicular to the osculating plane.

Since the equations of the tangent and of the osculating plane are known, the derivation of the equations of the principal normal and binormal does not present any difficulty and is left to the student as an exercise.

§ 4. **Contact of curves.** Suppose γ and γ' are elementary curves having a common point O. We choose the point P on the curve γ' and denote its distance from the curve γ by h and we denote the distance from P to the point O by d (see Fig. 5).

We shall say that the curve γ' has *contact of order n* with the curve γ at the point O if the ratio $h/d^n \to 0$ as $P \to O$.

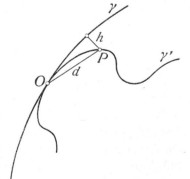

Fig. 5

Suppose γ and γ' are general curves having the common point O. We shall say that the curve γ' has contact of order n with the curve γ at the point O if an elementary neighborhood of the point O on the curve γ' has contact of order n with an elementary neighborhood of the curve γ.

THEOREM. *Suppose γ and γ' are regular plane curves, that $\varphi(x, y) = 0$ is the equation of the curve γ, and that $x = x(t), y = y(t)$ is the equation of the curve γ'. Suppose $\varphi_x{}^2 + \varphi_y{}^2 \neq 0$ at the point $O(x_0, y_0)$.*

Then a necessary and sufficient condition that the curve γ' have contact of order n with the curve γ at the point O is that the conditions

$$\varphi(x(t), y(t)) = 0, \frac{d}{dt} \varphi(x(t), y(t)) = 0, \cdots, \frac{d^n}{dt^n} \varphi(x(t), y(t)) = 0 \ be$$

satisfied for the value of t corresponding to the point O.

PROOF. Suppose $\bar{\gamma}$ is an elementary curve which is a neighborhood of the point O on the curve γ. Suppose $M(x, y)$ is any point in the x, y-plane, which is near the point O. The distance of the point M from the curve $\bar{\gamma}$ is the greatest lower bound of the distances of points on the curve to the point M. If the point M is sufficiently close to O, this greatest lower bound is attained for some point $\bar{M}(\bar{x}, \bar{y})$ on the curve. We shall show this.

Since the point O belongs to the curve γ, there exists an $\varepsilon > 0$ such that all the points in the plane which are at a distance not greater than ε from the point O and which satisfy the equation $\varphi(x, y) = 0$, belong to the curve γ.

Suppose the point M is at a distance less than $\varepsilon/2$ from the point O. Let $\bar{M}_n$ be a sequence of points on the curve γ whose distances from M tend to the distance of the point M from the curve γ. The points $\bar{M}_n$ form a bounded sequence (their distances from M are less than $\varepsilon/2$), and therefore this sequence contains a convergent subsequence. Without loss of generality, we may assume that the sequence $\bar{M}_n$ itself converges to some point $\bar{M}(\bar{x}, \bar{y})$. In virtue of the continuity of the function $\varphi(x, y)$ in a neighborhood of the point O, the point $\bar{M}$ satisfies the equation $\varphi(x, y) = 0$. From this it follows that the point $\bar{M}$ belongs to the curve γ. Thus, if the point M is sufficiently close to O, the greatest lower bound of the distances of the points on the curve γ from the point M is attained for some point $\bar{M}(\bar{x}, \bar{y})$ on the curve $\bar{\gamma}$.

We shall show that the segment $M\bar{M}$ is directed along the normal to the curve γ at the point $\bar{M}$. In fact, suppose $\bar{r}(s)$ is the position vector of a point on the curve γ, and that m is the position vector of the point M. The distance of the point M from points on the curve equals $\sqrt{(\bar{r}(s) - m)^2}$. For s, corresponding to the minimum of this distance, we have

$$\frac{d}{ds} \sqrt{(r(s) - m)^2} = 0,$$

and hence $(\bar{r}(s) - m) \cdot \bar{r}'(s) = 0$ which means that the vector $M\bar{M}$ is directed along the normal to the curve γ at the point $\bar{M}$.

Suppose ξ, η are the direction cosines of the straight line $M\bar{M}$. The coordinates of the point $\bar{M}$ can be expressed in the following way in terms of the coordinates of the point M:

$$\bar{x} = x + \xi h, \quad \bar{y} = y + \eta h,$$

where h is the distance of the point M from the curve γ.

The coordinates $\bar{x}$, $\bar{y}$ of the point $\bar{M}$, as points on the curves γ, satisfy the equation $\varphi(x, y) = 0$. Thus, we have

$$\varphi(x + \xi h, y + \eta h) = 0.$$

If follows that

$$\varphi(x, y) + \xi h \varphi_x(x, y) + \eta h \varphi_y(x, y) + h^2 R = 0,$$

where R is bounded in a neighborhood of the point $O(x_0, y_0)$.

As $x \to x_0$, $y \to y_0$ the expression $\xi \varphi_x + \eta \varphi_y$ tends to a limit, which is different from zero, inasmuch as it represents the scalar product of two vectors with coordinates ξ, η and φ_x, φ_y which in the limit are different from zero and directed along the normal to the curve γ at the point O. Thus, the quantity $h = -\dfrac{-\varphi}{\xi \varphi_x + \eta \varphi_y} + h^2 R'$ has order φ as $M \to O$.

Suppose M lies on the curve γ' and corresponds to the value t of the parameter. Then, its distance from O, equal to

$$|r(t) - r(t_0)| = |(t - t_0)(r'(t_0) + \varepsilon)|,$$

is of order $|t - t_0|$ when M is sufficiently close to O. From this it follows that a necessary and sufficient condition that the curve γ' have contact of order n with the curve γ at the point O is that

$$\frac{\varphi(x(t), y(t))}{(t - t_0)^n} \to 0$$

as $t \rightarrow t_0$. But this means that all the terms in the expansion of the function $\varphi(x(t), y(t))$ involving powers of $(t - t_0)$ up to the n-th inclusive, equal zero.

This completes the proof of the theorem.

EXAMPLE. Suppose $\gamma_{\alpha_1, \alpha_2, \ldots, \alpha_n}$ is a given family of curves, depending on n parameters $\alpha_1, \alpha_2, \cdots, \alpha_n$, defined by the equations $\varphi(x, y, \alpha_1, \cdots, \alpha_n) = 0$, and that the curve γ is defined by the equations $x = x(t)$, $y = y(t)$.

Find a curve among this family of curves with which the curve γ has contact of order $n - 1$ at the given point O.

In agreement with the theorem we proved above, if the curve γ has contact of order $n - 1$ with the curve $\gamma_{\alpha_1, \ldots, \alpha_n}$ at the point O, then

$$\varphi = 0, \frac{d}{dt} \varphi = 0, \quad \cdots, \quad \frac{d^{(n-1)}}{dt^{n-1}} \varphi = 0$$

for the value of t corresponding to the point O.

From this system we find the values of the parameters $\alpha_1, \alpha_2, \cdots, \alpha_n$, for which the curve γ has the indicated property.

§ 5. Envelope of a family of curves, depending on a parameter.

Suppose $S\{\gamma_\alpha\}$ is a family of smooth curves on a surface, depending on a parameter α. A smooth curve γ is called an *envelope* of the family S if a) for every point on the curve γ it is possible to give a curve γ_α of the family which is tangent to the curve γ at this point, b) for every curve γ_α of the family it is possible to give a point on the curve γ at which the curve γ_α is tangent to γ, c) no curve of the family has a segment in common with the curve γ (Fig. 6).

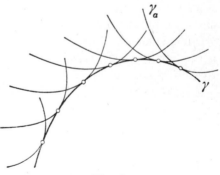

Fig. 6

EXAMPLE. A smooth curve not having rectilinear arcs is the envelope of its tangents.

The following theorem solves, to a known degree, the problem of finding the envelope.

THEOREM. *Suppose the curves γ_α of a family S are given by the equations $\varphi(x, y, \alpha) = 0$, where φ is continuous and continuously differentiable for all its arguments.*

Then the envelope of the family S is given by the equations

$$\varphi(x, y, \alpha) = 0, \quad \varphi_\alpha(x, y, \alpha) = 0$$

in the sense that for every point (x, y) of the envelope one can find an α such that both equations $\varphi = 0$ and $\varphi_\alpha = 0$ will be satisfied by the system of values x, y, α.

The proof of this theorem in the form we have just formulated it, although carried out by elementary methods of analysis, is obtained in a rather cumbersome fashion. In this connection, in order to simplify the discussion, we shall make some additional assumptions about the nature of the enveloping of the curve by curves of the family. Namely, we shall assume that for every point P of the curve γ it is possible to give an interval Δ_P of variation of the parameter α such that:

1) For every point Q of the curve γ, near P, there exists only one curve of the family with parameter α, belonging to Δ_P, and tangent to the curve at the point Q;

2) If $r = r(t)$ is any smooth parametrization of the curve γ in a neighborhood of the point P and $\gamma_{\alpha(t)}$ is a curve of the family tangent to γ at the point (t) (where $\alpha(t)$ belongs to Δ_P), then $\alpha(t)$ is a smooth function of t.

Under such additional hypotheses on the nature of the enveloping of the curve γ by curves of the family, the proof of the theorem is rather simple.

Since the curve γ is tangent to the $\gamma_{\alpha(t)}$ of the family at the point (t), the following identity holds:

$$\varphi(x(t), y(t), \alpha(t)) \equiv 0.$$

Differentiating this identity with respect to t, we obtain

$$\varphi_x x' + \varphi_y y' + \varphi_\alpha \alpha' = 0.$$

Since the curves γ and $\gamma_{\alpha(t)}$ are tangent at the point (t), we have $\varphi_x x' + \varphi_y y' = 0$. Therefore, we have $\varphi_\alpha \alpha' = 0$.

We shall assume that $\varphi_\alpha \neq 0$ at the point P. Then $\varphi_\alpha \neq 0$ also in some neighborhood of the point P, and hence $\alpha' = 0$ in this neighborhood, i.e. $\alpha(t) = \text{constant} = c$. But this means that the envelope

γ has a common segment with the curve γ_c, which is impossible. Thus, $\varphi_\alpha = 0$ at the point P. This completes the proof of the theorem.

REMARK. The system of equations

$$\varphi(x, y, \alpha) = 0, \quad \varphi_\alpha(x, y, \alpha) = 0$$

can, in general, also be satisfied by curves which are not envelopes. For example, the equation of the envelope to the family of curves

$$(x - \alpha)^3 + (y - \alpha)^3 - 3(x - \alpha)(y - \alpha) = 0,$$

is satisfied by the line $x = y$, which however is not an envelope. This straight line consists of nodal points of the curves of the family (Fig. 7).

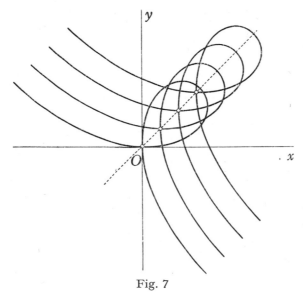

Fig. 7

EXERCISES FOR CHAPTER II

1. Write the equations of the a) tangent, b) osculating plane, c) normal plane, d) principal normal, e) binormal to the helix

$$x = \cos t, \quad y = \sin t, \quad z = t$$

at the point $(1, 0, 0)$.

ANSWER: a) equation of the tangent: $\dfrac{x - 1}{0} = \dfrac{y}{1} = \dfrac{z}{1}$;

b) equation of the osculating plane: $y - z = 0$;

c) equation of the normal plane: $y + z = 0$;

d) equation of the principal normal: $y = z = 0$;

e) equation of the binormal: $\dfrac{x-1}{0} = \dfrac{y}{1} = \dfrac{z}{-1}$.

2. Write the equation of the tangent to the curve defined by the equations

$$x^2 + y^2 + z^2 = 1, \quad x^2 + y^2 = x$$

at the point $(0, 0, 1)$.

ANSWER: $\dfrac{x}{0} = \dfrac{y}{1} = \dfrac{z-1}{0}$.

3. Find the equation of the parabola of the form $y = x^2 + ax + b$ which is tangent to the circle $x^2 + y^2 = 2$ at the point $(1, 1)$.

ANSWER: $y = x^2 - 3x + 3$.

4. Find the curve $y = y(x)$ if it is known that the length of the segment of the tangent between the point of tangency and the point of intersection of the tangent with the x-axis is constant and equal to a.

ANSWER: Tractrix:

$$c \pm x = a \ln \frac{a - \sqrt{a^2 - y^2}}{y} + \sqrt{a^2 - y^2}.$$

5. Segments of the same length are marked off on the binormals of a simple helix. Find the equation of the curve generated by the endpoints of these segments.

ANSWER: Helix.

6. What is the angle at which the curves

$$xy = c_1, \quad x^2 - y^2 = c_2$$

intersect?

ANSWER: $\pi/2$.

7. If the curve γ in a plane intersects the curves of the family

$$\varphi(x, y) = \text{constant} \quad (\varphi_x^2 + \varphi_y^2 \neq 0)$$

orthogonally, then it satisfies the equation

$$\frac{dx}{\varphi_x} = \frac{dy}{\varphi_y}.$$

Prove this assertion.

8. Find the family of curves which intersect all circles passing through two given points in the plane orthogonally.

ANSWER: A family of circles.

9. Find the equation of the circles having contact of the second order with the parabola $y = x^2$ at its vertex.

ANSWER: $x^2 + y^2 = y$.

10. Find the envelope of the family of straight lines which form a triangle XOY of area $2a^2$ with the coordinates axes.

ANSWER: The part of the equilateral hyperbola $xy = a^2$ which lies in the angle XOY.

11. Find the envelope of the family of straight lines on which the coordinate axes cut off a segment of constant length a.

ANSWER: Astroid:

$$|x|^{2/3} + |y|^{2/3} = a^{2/3}.$$

12. Find the envelope of the trajectories of a material point ejected from the origin of coordinates with initial velocity v_0.

ANSWER: The trajectory parabola

$$y = -\frac{gx^2}{2v_0^2} + \frac{v_0^2}{2g}$$

where g is the acceleration due to gravity.

13. Find the envelope of light rays emanating from the origin of the coordinate system after their reflexion from the circle $x^2 + y^2 = 2ax$.

ANSWER: The Pascal limaçon:

$$(x^2 + y^2 - 2ax)^2 + \frac{4a^2}{3}\left(x^2 + y^2 - \frac{16ax}{9}\right) = 0.$$

PROBLEMS AND THEOREMS FOR CHAPTER II

1. Suppose γ is a curve and that P is a point on γ, and suppose g is a straight line passing through the two distinct points R and S on the curve. We say that the curve has a tangent at the point P in the strong sense if the straight lines g converge to some straight line g_P as $R, S \to P$.

Prove that if the curve is smooth, then it has a tangent in the strong sense at every point, and this tangent coincides with the tangent in the sense of the usual definition, given in § 2.

If the curve has a tangent in the strong sense at every point, then the curve is smooth.

2. Prove that if the tangents to a smooth curve pass through a common point, then the curve is a segment of a straight line, or half-line, or an entire line.

3. Prove that the tangents to the helix

$$x = a \cos \omega t, \quad y = a \sin \omega t, \quad z = bt$$

are inclined at a constant angle to the x, y-plane. Show that the principal normals to the helix intersect the z-axis.

4. An inversion is a transformation under which corresponding points are located on the same half-line emanating from some fixed point S (called the center of inversion), and the product of their distances from S is constant. Prove that the angle between curves remains invariant under an inversion.

5. Prove that if the tangents to a curve are parallel to some plane, then the curve is a plane curve.

6. What is the condition that the straight line g_t:

$$\begin{cases} a_1(t)x + b_1(t)y + c_1(t)z + d_1(t) = 0, \\ a_2(t)x + b_2(t)y + c_2(t)z + d_2(t) = 0 \end{cases}$$

be tangent to some curve

$$x = x(t), \quad y = y(t), \quad z = z(t)?$$

Find this curve.

7. Write the equation of the osculating plane to the curve defined by the equations

$$\varphi(x, y, z) = 0, \quad \psi(x, y, z) = 0$$

at the point (x_0, y_0, z_0).

8. Suppose γ is a curve and that P is a point on γ; let α be a plane passing through distinct points Q, R and S on the curve. We say that the curve γ has an osculating plane at the point P in the strong sense if the planes α tend to some plane α_P as Q, R, $S \to P$.

Prove that if a regular (i.e. twice continuously differentiable) curve has a unique osculating plane at the point P in the usual sense (§ 3), then it has an osculating plane at this point in the strong sense and they coincide.

9. Reconstruct the curve $x = x(t), y = y(t), z = z(t)$ knowing that

its osculating planes are
$$A(t)x + B(t)y + C(t)z + D(t) = 0.$$

10. Prove that if all the osculating planes of a curve pass through a common point, then the curve is a plane curve.

11. Prove that a necessary and sufficient condition that the curve $x = x(t)$, $y = y(t)$, $z = z(t)$ be a plane curve is that

$$\begin{vmatrix} x' & y' & z' \\ x'' & y'' & z'' \\ x''' & y''' & z''' \end{vmatrix} \equiv 0.$$

12. Prove that the contact property of curves is mutual, i.e. if the smooth curve γ_1 has contact of order n with the smooth curve γ_2 then the curve γ_2 has contact of order n with the curve γ_1 at the same point.

Show by an example that the smoothness requirement is essential.

13. Assume the curves γ_1, γ_2, γ_3 have a common point P at which the curves γ_1 and γ_2, γ_2 and γ_3 have contact of order n. Then the curves γ_1 and γ_3 also have contact of order n at the point P.

14. Prove that if a curve has contact of order three with its osculating plane at every point, then this curve is a plane curve.

15. A projective correspondence

$$y = \frac{\alpha x + \beta}{\gamma x + \delta}, \quad \alpha\delta - \beta\gamma \neq 0$$

is established between the points of the x and y coordinate axes.

Prove that the family of straight lines joining corresponding points on the axes, envelope a second degree curve.

16. Prove that if a one parameter family of curves in the plane is given by the equations

$$\varphi(x, y, \alpha, \beta) = 0, \quad f(\alpha, \beta) = 0,$$

where $f_\alpha{}^2 + f_\beta{}^2 \neq 0$, then the envelope of this family satisfies the equations

$$\varphi = 0, \quad f = 0, \quad \varphi_\alpha + \lambda f_\alpha = 0, \quad \varphi_\beta + \lambda f_\beta = 0$$

in the sense that for every point (x, y) of the envelope, one can find α, β and λ which are such that together with x and y they satisfy the above four equations.

The equation of the envelope in the implicit form can be obtained by eliminating α, β, λ from these four equations.

CHAPTER III

FUNDAMENTAL CONCEPTS FOR CURVES WHICH ARE RELATED TO THE CONCEPTS OF CURVATURE AND TORSION

§ 1. Concept of arc length of a curve. Suppose γ is an arbitrary curve. In § 3 of Chapter I we showed that γ is the image of an open interval g or of a circumference k under a continuous and locally one-to-one mapping φ into space.

A *segment* of the curve γ is the image of an arbitrary closed segment Δ, belonging to the open interval g or to the arc κ of the circumference k under the mapping φ. The endpoints of the segment of the curve are the images of the endpoints of the open interval Δ or the endpoints of the arc κ of the circumference.

The concept of a segment of a curve thus introduced does not depend on the mapping in the sense that if the mappings φ_1 and φ_2 of the open interval g or of the circumference k define the same curve γ then the set of segments of the curve defined by the mappings φ_1 and φ_2 coincide. We shall prove this.

Suppose the mappings φ_1 and φ_2 of the open interval g define the same curve γ. In agreement with the definition given in § 3 of Chapter I, this means that there exists a one-to-one and bicontinuous correspondence ψ between the points of the open interval g for which the images of corresponding points under the mappings φ_1 and φ_2 coincide.

Suppose $\Delta_1(a \leq t \leq b)$ is any closed interval belonging to g and that $\varphi_1(\Delta_1)$ is its image under the mapping φ_1. We most prove the existence of a segment Δ_2, whose image is $\varphi_2(\Delta_2)$ under the mapping φ_2 coincides with $\varphi_1(\Delta_1)$.

We shall denote the image of the segment Δ_1 under the mapping ψ of the open interval g onto itself by Δ'. We shall show that Δ' is a closed interval. In fact, the function $\psi(t)$ which effects the mapping of the open interval g onto itself, is continuous on the segment $\Delta_1(a \leq t \leq b)$. It follows from this that this function attains its maximum M, its minimum m and assumes all intermediate values on the segment Δ_1. But this means that Δ' is the closed interval

$m \leq t \leq M$. The images of the closed segments $\varDelta_1$ and $\varDelta'$ under the mappings φ_1 and φ_2 respectively yield the same segment of the curve. This completes the proof of our assertion.

The set of points on a segment of a curve can be ordered in the following way. Suppose $\varphi(A)$, $\varphi(B)$, $\varphi(C)$ are three points on a segment of the curve. We shall say that the point $\varphi(B)$ lies *between* the points $\varphi(A)$ and $\varphi(C)$ if the points on the segment $\varDelta$ or the arc of the circumference corresponding to them are in this relation.

It follows from the preceding discussion on the independence of the concept of segment of the mapping φ which determines the curve γ that the "betweenness" relation for points of the segment is also independent of φ. In fact, a continuous function $\psi(t)$ which assumes distinct values for distinct t is a monotonic function. It follows from this that if A', B', C' are points of the segment $\varDelta'$ corresponding to A, B, C, then B' lies between A' and C'. But this means that the mappings φ_1 and φ_2 of the open interval g, which define the same curve, also define the same "betweenness" relationship for the points of its segment.

In conclusion we note that the property of points of being the endpoints of a segment of a curve is also independent of the mapping φ, which determines the curve. In fact, if the curve γ is defined with the aid of φ_1 then the endpoints of the segment $\varphi_1(\varDelta_1)$ are the images of the endpoints of the segment $\varDelta_1$ under the mapping φ_1; if the curve γ is defined by means of φ_2 then the endpoints of the segment $\varphi_1(\varDelta_1) \equiv \varphi_2(\varDelta')$ are the images of the endpoints of the segment $\varDelta'$ under the mapping φ_2. But in virtue of the monotonicity of the function $\psi(t)$ the endpoints of the segments $\varDelta_1$ and $\varDelta'$ correspond to each other under the mapping ψ and the images of corresponding points of the segments $\varDelta_1$ and $\varDelta'$ coincide under the mappings φ_1 and φ_2. This is what we were required to prove.

We now define the concept of arc length of a segment of a curve.

Suppose $\tilde{\gamma}$ is a segment of the curve γ and let A and B be its endpoints. We choose

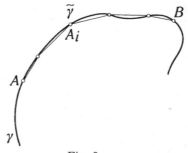

Fig. 8

the points $A_0 \equiv A$, A_1, $\cdots$, $A_n \equiv B$, on the segment $\tilde{\gamma}$, proceeding from A to B in the sense that the point A_i lies between A_{i-1} and A_{i+1}. We join successive points A_i and A_{i+1} by means of rectilinear segments. We then obtain the polygonal arc Γ inscribed in the segment $\tilde{\gamma}$ of the curve (see Fig. 8).

We shall say that the segment $\tilde{\gamma}$ of the curve γ is *rectifiable* if the lengths of the polygonal arcs Γ are uniformly bounded. The least upper bound of the lengths of the polygonal arcs Γ, inscribed in the segment $\tilde{\gamma}$ of the curve, will be called the *arc length*, or simply the *arc*, of this segment. We shall say that the curve γ is rectifiable if each of its segments is rectifiable. The length of the arc will be the least upper bound of the arc lengths of its segments.

We shall show that arc length so introduced possesses the usual properties, namely:

1. If the segment $A'B'$ of the curve γ is a subset of the segment AB and if the segment AB is rectifiable, then the segment $A'B'$ is also rectifiable and the length of its arc $s(A'B')$ is less than the arc length $s(AB)$ of the segment AB.

2. If C is a point on the segment AB of the curve γ which is distinct from both A and B, and the segments AC and CB are rectifiable, then the segment AB is also rectifiable, and

$$s(AC) + s(CB) = s(AB).$$

PROOF. Since the segment $A'B'$ is a subset of the segment AB, then one of the points A' and B' (for definiteness, let us say it is

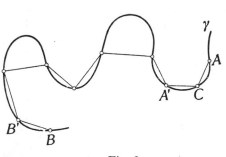

Fig. 9

the point A') is not an endpoint of the segment AB. Suppose Γ'' is an arbitrary polygonal arc, inscribed in the segment $A'B'$ of the curve, and suppose C is an arbitrary point of the segment AA', which is geometrically distinct from A and A' (Fig. 9). Adding the new vertices A, C and B to the polygonal arc Γ'', we obtain the polygonal arc Γ inscribed in the segment AB of the curve γ. The length of the polygonal arc Γ is greater than the length of Γ'' by at least the sum of the lengths of the links AC and CA'. Since the polygonal arc Γ' was taken arbitrarily, this means that the lengths of the polygonal arcs Γ' are uniformly bounded and, consequently, the segment $A'B'$ of the curve γ is rectifiable. The length of this segment, obviously, is less than the length of the segment AB of the curve by at least the sum of the lengths of the links AC and CA'.

We shall now prove the second property. Suppose Γ is an arbitrary polygonal arc inscribed in the segment AB of the curve. We add the vertex C to it. The polygonal arc $\bar{\Gamma}$ thus obtained has length greater than or equal to that of the polygonal arc Γ. This polygonal arc consists of the polygonal arcs Γ' and Γ'' inscribed in the segments AC and CB of the curve γ. It follows from this that the segment AB is rectifiable and that

$$s(AC) + s(CB) \geq s(AB).$$

Now suppose Γ' and Γ''' are arbitrary polygonal arcs inscribed in the segments AC respectively CB of the curve. Then the polygonal arc Γ, consisting of the polygonal arcs Γ' and Γ''', will be inscribed in the segment AB of the curve γ. It follows from this that

$$s(AC) + s(CB) \leq s(AB).$$

Combining this with the preceding inequality we obtain

$$s(AC) + s(CB) = s(AB),$$

which was to be proved.

§ 2. Arc length of a smooth curve. Natural parametrization of a curve.

THEOREM. *A smooth curve γ is rectifiable. If $r = r(t)$ is its smooth parametrization and $\bar{\gamma}(a \leq t \leq b)$ is a segment of the curve γ then the length of this segment is*

$$s(\bar{\gamma}) = \int_a^b |r'(t)| \, dt.$$

PROOF. Suppose Γ is an arbitrary polygonal arc inscribed in the segment $\bar{\gamma}$ of the curve γ. Let $t_1 = a, t_2, \cdots, t_{n+1} = b$ be the values of the parameter t corresponding to its vertices. The length of the link of the polygonal arc joining the vertices t_i and t_{i+1} equals $|r(t_{i+1}) - r(t_i)|$. Therefore the length of the entire polygonal arc is

$$s(\Gamma) = \sum_{i=1}^n |r(t_{i+1}) - r(t_i)|.$$

We now estimate the length of the polygonal arc Γ. We have

$$|r(t_{i+1}) - r(t_i)| \leq |x(t_{i+1}) - x(t_i)| + |y(t_{i+1}) - y(t_i)| +$$
$$+ |z(t_{i+1}) - z(t_i)| = (t_{i+1} - t_i)(|x'(\vartheta_i')| + |y'(\vartheta_i'')| + |z'(\vartheta_i'')|),$$

where ϑ_i', ϑ_i'', ϑ_i''' lie between t_i and t_{i+1}. Since the derivatives $x'(t)$, $y'(t)$, $z'(t)$ are bounded by some constant M on the closed interval $a \leq t \leq b$, and

$$\Sigma_{i=1}^n (t_{i+1} - t_i) = b - a,$$

we have

$$s(\Gamma) \leq 3M(b - a).$$

Thus, the lengths of the polygonal arcs Γ inscribed in the segment $\tilde{\gamma}$ of the curve γ, are uniformly bounded and, consequently, the segment $\tilde{\gamma}$ is rectifiable. Since the segment $\tilde{\gamma}$ was chosen arbitrarily, we conclude the curve γ is also rectifiable.

REMARK. In the proof of the rectifiability of the segment $\tilde{\gamma}$ of the curve we used the fact that there existed a smooth parametrization for every segment, whereas the smoothness of the curve, by definition, assumes only the existence of such a parametrization only in a neighborhood of each point of the curve. In order not to use only one smooth parametrization for the entire segment $\tilde{\gamma}$, we proceed in the following manner.

We shall start with any parametrization $r = r(t)$ of the curve γ. Suppose $\bar{a} \leq t \leq \bar{b}$ is a segment of γ. We decompose the segment γ by means of the points $\bar{a} + k \dfrac{\bar{b} - \bar{a}}{n}$ $(k = 1, 2, \cdots, n - 1)$ into n segments. If n is sufficiently large, each of these segments permits a smooth parametrization. In fact, let us assume the contrary. Suppose a segment $t_n' t_n''$ can be found for every n which does not permit a smooth parametrization. The sequence of segments $t_n' t_n''$ contains a subsequence of segments whose endpoints t_n' and t_n'' converge, obviously to a common limit t_0. But the point t_0 has a neighborhood which permits a smooth parametrization. For sufficiently large n the segment $t_n' t_n''$ lies in this neighborhood and, consequently, it permits a smooth parametrization. We have thus arrived at a contradiction. Thus, for sufficiently large n the segment $\tilde{\gamma}$ will be decomposed into n segments, each of which permits a smooth parametrization and hence it is rectifiable by what was proved above. But then, as was proved in the preceding section, the segment $\tilde{\gamma}$ is also rectifiable.

We shall find the length of the segment $\tilde{\gamma}$, which permits a smooth parametrization $r = r(t)$.

We inscribe the polygonal arc Γ into the segment $\tilde{\gamma}$, satisfying the following conditions: 1) the length of the polygonal arc Γ differs from the arc length of the segment $\tilde{\gamma}$ by at most ε; 2) for all i $|t_{i+1} - t_i| < \delta$. Here ε and δ are arbitrary positive numbers. The existence of such a polygonal arc is quite obvious. In fact, there exists a polygonal arc Γ satisfying the first condition by the definition of the arc length of the segment of a curve. Adding new vertices to it, we do not invalidate the first condition. But at the same time the addition of new vertices helps us satisfy the second condition also.

We now estimate the length of an arbitrary link of the polygonal arc. We have

$$|r(t_{i+1}) - r(t_i)| = |(x(t_{i+1}) - x(t_i))e_1 + (y(t_{i+1}) - y(t_i))e_2 +$$
$$+ (z(t_{i+1}) - z(t_i))e_3| = (t_{i+1} - t_i)|x'(\vartheta_i')e_1 + y'(\vartheta_i'')e_2 + z'(\vartheta_i''')e_3| =$$
$$(t_{i+1} - t_i)|(x'(t_i) + \varepsilon_i')e_1 + (y'(t_i) + \varepsilon_i'')e_2 + (z'(t_i) + \varepsilon_i''')e_3|.$$

In virtue of the uniform continuity of the functions $x'(t)$, $y'(t)$, $z'(t)$ on the closed interval $a \leq t \leq b$ the quantities ε_i', ε_i'', ε_i''' are less than some $\bar{\varepsilon}(\delta)$, where $\bar{\varepsilon}(\delta) \to 0$ as $\delta \to 0$. Therefore

$$|r(t_{i+1}) - r(t_i)| = (t_{i+1} - t_i)|r'(t_i)| + (t_{i+1} - t_i)\eta_i,$$

where $|\eta_i|$ is less than some $\bar{\varepsilon}(\delta)$ which tends to zero as $\delta \to 0$.

Now suppose that Γ_n is a sequence of polygonal arcs inscribed in the segment $\tilde{\gamma}$, for which

$$s(\Gamma_n) \to s(\tilde{\gamma}) \text{ and } \delta_n \to 0.$$

The length of the polygonal arc is

$$s(\Gamma_n) = \sum (t_{i+1} - t_i)|r'(t_i)| + \sum (t_{i+1} - t_i)\eta_i.$$

As $n \to \infty$,

$$\sum (t_{i+1} - t_i)|r'(t_i)| \to \int_a^b |r'(t)|dt,$$

and $\sum (t_{i+1} - t_i)\eta_i \to 0$ inasmuch as $\sum (t_{i+1} - t_i) = b - a$, and $|\eta_i| < \bar{\varepsilon}(\delta_n)$.

Thus the arc length of the segment $\tilde{\gamma}$ of the curve γ is

$$s(\tilde{\gamma}) = \int_a^b |r'(t)|dt.$$

This completes the proof of the theorem.

Suppose γ is a rectifiable curve and let $r = r(t)$ be any one of its parametrizations. Suppose $s(t)$ is the arc length of the segment $t_0\,t$ of the curve γ. We shall define the function $\sigma(t)$ by means of the conditions

$$\sigma(t) = s(t) \quad \text{if } t_0 < t;$$
$$\sigma(t) = -\,s(t) \text{ if } t_0 > t;$$
$$\sigma(t_0) = 0.$$

The function $\sigma(t)$ is strictly monotonic. Therefore σ can be taken as the parameter on the curve. We shall call this parametrization the *natural* parametrization.

THEOREM. *The natural parametrization of a regular (k-times differentiable, analytic) curve without singular points is regular (k-times differentiable respectively analytic). If $r = r(\sigma)$ is the natural parametrization of the curve then $|r'(\sigma)| = 1$.*

PROOF. Suppose $r = \tilde{r}(t)$ is any regular parametrization of the curve γ in a neighborhood of an arbitrary point corresponding to the value σ_1 of the parameter. For each segment belonging to this neighborhood we have

$$\sigma - \sigma_1 = \int_{t_1}^{t_2} \sqrt{\tilde{r}'^2(t)}\,dt.$$

Since $d\sigma/dt = \sqrt{\tilde{r}'^2(t)} > 0$ and $\tilde{r}(t)$ is a k-times differentiable function of t, t is a k-times differentiable function of σ. But for σ close to σ_1, $r(\sigma) = \tilde{r}(t(\sigma))$. It follows from this that $r(\sigma)$ is a regular (k-times differentiable) function and

$$\frac{dr(\sigma)}{d\sigma} = \frac{dr(t)}{dt}\frac{dt}{d\sigma} = \frac{d\tilde{r}(t)}{dt}\frac{1}{\left|\dfrac{d\tilde{r}(t)}{dt}\right|}.$$

Consequently, $|r'(\sigma)| = 1$.

This concludes the proof of the theorem.

COROLLARY. *A regular (k-times differentiable, analytic) curve permits a regular (k-times differentiable respectively analytic) parametrization "in the large", i.e. for the entire curve.*

Such a parametrization is the natural parametrization r(σ) and also any parametrization obtained from it by means of a regular transformation of the parameter σ = φ(t), where φ(t) is a regular (respectively analytic) function of t which satisfies the condition that φ'(t) ≠ 0.

To conclude this section, we shall give the formulas for arc length of a regular curve for two different ways of analytically determining the curve.

1. For a curve defined by the equations

$$x = x(t), \quad y = y(t), \quad z = z(t),$$

the arc length is

$$s(t_1, t_2) = \int_{t_1}^{t_2} |r'(t)| dt = \int_{t_1}^{t_2} \sqrt{x'^2 + y'^2 + z'^2} \, dt.$$

2. A curve defined by the equations

$$y = y(x), \quad z = z(x)$$

has arc length

$$s(x_1, x_2) = \int_{x_1}^{x_2} \sqrt{1 + y'^2 + z'^2} dx.$$

For plane curves, lying in the x, y-plane, we must set $z' = 0$ in these two formulas.

§ 3. Curvature of a curve.

Suppose P is an arbitrary point on the regular curve γ and Q is a point on γ near P. We denote the angle between the tangents drawn to the curve at P and Q by $\Delta\vartheta$ and the arc length of the segment PQ of the curve by Δs (Fig. 10).

The *curvature* of a curve γ at the point P is the limit of the ratio $\Delta\vartheta/\Delta s$ as the point Q approaches P.

Then the following theorem holds.

THEOREM. *A regular (twice continuously differentiable) curve has a definite curvature k_1 at each of its points. If*

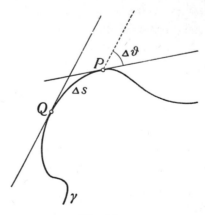

Fig. 10

$r = r(s)$ *is the natural parametrization of the curve, then*

$$k_1 = |r''(s)|.$$

Suppose the values s and $s + \Delta s$ of the parameter correspond to the points P and Q. The angle $\Delta\vartheta$ is equal to the angle between the unit tangent vectors $\tau(s) = r'(s)$ and $\tau(s + \Delta s) = r'(s + \Delta s)$.

Since the vectors $\tau(s)$ and $\tau(s + \Delta s)$ are unit vectors and form the angle $\Delta\vartheta$, $|\tau(s + \Delta s) - \tau(s)| = 2\sin\dfrac{\Delta\vartheta}{2}$. Therefore

$$\frac{|\tau(s + \Delta s) - \tau(s)|}{\Delta s} = \frac{2\sin\dfrac{\Delta\vartheta}{2}}{\Delta s} = \frac{\sin\dfrac{\Delta\vartheta}{2}}{\dfrac{\Delta\vartheta}{2}}\frac{\Delta\vartheta}{\Delta s}.$$

Noting that $\Delta\vartheta \to 0$ as $\Delta s \to 0$ and passing to the limit, we obtain

$$|r''(s)| = k_1.$$

This completes the proof of the theorem.

Suppose the curvature does not vanish at a given point on a curve. Consider the vector $n = (1/k_1)r''(s)$. The vector n is a unit vector and lies in the osculating plane of the curve (§ 3, Chapter II). Moreover, this vector is perpendicular to the tangent vector τ, so that $\tau^2 = 1$ and, consequently $\tau\cdot\tau' = \tau\cdot\eta k_1 = 0$. Thus, this vector is directed along the principal normal to the curve. Obviously, the direction of the vector n does not change if the initial point of the arc s or the direction of traversing s is changed. In the sequel, when we mention the unit vector on the principal normal to the curve, we shall have in mind the vector n.

Obviously, the vector $\tau \times n = b$ is directed along the binormal of the curve. This vector will be called the unit binormal vector of the curve.

We shall find an expression for the curvature of a curve in the case of an arbitrary parametric representation. Suppose the curve is given by the vector equation $r = r(t)$. We shall express the second derivative of the vector function r with respect to the arc s in terms of the derivatives with respect to t. We have

$$r' = r_s s'.$$

It follows that

$$r'^2 = s'^2$$

and consequently

$$r_s' = r'/\sqrt{r'^2}.$$

Differentiating this equality once more with respect to t, we obtain

$$r_{ss}s' = r''/\sqrt{r'^2} - (r' \cdot r'')r'/(\sqrt{r'^2})^3.$$

Squaring both sides of this equality and noting that $s'^2 = r'^2$, we have

$$k_1^2 = \frac{r''^2 r'^2 - (r' \cdot r'')^2}{(r'^2)^3}$$

or, what amounts to the same thing,

$$k_1^2 = \frac{(r' \times r'')^2}{(r'^2)^3}.$$

From this we obtain that the curvature of a curve given by the equations

$$x = x(t), \quad y = y(t), \quad z = z(t)$$

is defined by

$$k_1^2 = \frac{\begin{vmatrix} x'' & y'' \\ x' & y' \end{vmatrix}^2 + \begin{vmatrix} y'' & z'' \\ y' & z' \end{vmatrix}^2 + \begin{vmatrix} z'' & x'' \\ z' & x' \end{vmatrix}^2}{(x'^2 + y'^2 + z'^2)^3}.$$

If the curve is a plane curve lying in the x, y-plane,

$$k_1^2 = \frac{(x''y' - y''x')^2}{(x'^2 + y'^2)^3}.$$

If the plane curve is given by the equation $y = y(x)$,

$$k_1^2 = \frac{y''^2}{(1 + y'^2)^3}.$$

REMARK. The curvature of a curve is, by definition, nonnegative. For plane curves, it is convenient in many cases to choose the sign of curvature so that in some cases it is positive and in others negative. The tangent vector $r'(t)$ of the curve rotates as it moves along the curve in the direction of increasing t. Depending on the direction of rotation of the vector $r'(t)$ the curvature is considered positive or negative. If we determine the sign of the curvature of a plane curve by this condition, then we obtain the following formulas for it:

$$k = \frac{x''y' - y''x'}{(x'^2 + y'^2)^{3/2}} \quad \text{or} \quad k = -\frac{x''y' - y''x'}{(x'^2 + y'^2)^{3/2}}.$$

In particular, if the curve is given in the form $y = y(x)$,

$$k = y''/(1 + y'^2)^{3/2} \quad \text{or} \quad k = -y''/(1 + y'^2)^{3/2}.$$

In conclusion, we find all the curves having curvature zero at all its points. We have

$$k_1 = |r''(s)| = 0.$$

It follows that $r''(s) = 0$ and, consequently, $r(s) = as + b$, where a and b are constant vectors.

Thus, a curve having curvature everywhere equal to zero is either a straight line or an open interval on a straight line. The converse is also true.

§ 4. Torsion of a curve.

Suppose P is an arbitrary point on the curve γ and Q is a point on γ near P. We denote the angle between the osculating planes to the curve at the points P and Q by $\Delta\vartheta$ and we denote the length of the segment PQ on the curve by Δs. The *absolute torsion* $|k_2|$ of the curve γ at the point P is understood to be the limit of the ratio $\Delta\vartheta/\Delta s$ as $Q \to P$.

THEOREM. *A regular (three-times continuously differentiable) curve has a definite absolute torsion $|k_2|$ at every point where the curvature is different from zero. If $r = r(s)$ is the natural parametrization of the curve, then*

$$|k_2| = |(r'r''r''')|/k_1^2.$$

PROOF. If the curvature of the curve γ at the point P is different from zero, then by continuity it is different from zero at all points sufficiently close to P. At every point where the curvature differs from zero, the vectors $r'(s)$ and $r''(s)$ are different from zero and are not parallel. Therefore, a definite osculating plane exists at each point Q near P.

Suppose $b(s)$ and $b(s + \Delta s)$ are unit binormal vectors at the points P and Q on the curve γ. The angle $\Delta\vartheta$ is equal to the angle between the vectors $b(s)$ and $b(s + \Delta s)$.

Since the vectors $b(s)$ and $b(s + \Delta s)$ are unit vectors and form the angle $\Delta\vartheta$, $|b(s + \Delta s) - b(s)| = 2 \sin \dfrac{\Delta\vartheta}{2}$. Therefore

$$\frac{|b(s + \Delta s) \quad b(s)|}{\Delta s} = \frac{2 \sin \dfrac{\Delta\vartheta}{2}}{\Delta s} = \frac{\sin \dfrac{\Delta\vartheta}{2}}{\dfrac{\Delta\vartheta}{2}} \frac{\Delta\vartheta}{\Delta s} .$$

From this we obtain, passing to the limit as $\Delta s \to 0$, that

$$|k_2| = |b'|.$$

The vector b' is perpendicular to b since $b' \cdot b = (\frac{1}{2}b^2)' = 0$. It is not difficult to see that b' is also perpendicular to τ.

In fact,

$$b' = (\tau \times n)' = \tau' \times n + \tau \times n'.$$

But $\tau' \| n$. Therefore, $b' = \tau \times n'$, whence it follows that b' is perpendicular to τ. Thus, the vector b' is parallel to the vector n and, consequently,

$$|k_2| = |b' \cdot n|.$$

If we set $n = (1/k)r''$ and $b = r' \times r''/k_1$ into this last equation, we obtain

$$|k_2| = |(r'r''r''')|/k_1{}^2.$$

This completes the proof of the theorem.

We shall now define the *torsion* of a curve.

It follows from the fact that the vectors b' and n are parallel that the osculating plane to the curve rotates about the tangent to the curve as it moves along the curve in the direction of increasing s. In this connection, we define the torsion of a curve by means of the equation

$$k_2 = \pm |k_2|$$

and we shall take the sign $(+)$ if the rotation of the tangent plane occurs in the direction from b to n, and $(-)$ if the rotation occurs in the direction from n to b. If we define the torsion of a curve in this way, we shall have $k_2 = b' \cdot n$ or

$$k_2 = - (r'r''r''')/k_1{}^2.$$

We shall now find the expression for the torsion of a curve in the case when it is defined by an arbitrary regular parametrization $r = r(t)$. We have

$$r_s = r't', \quad r_{ss} = r''t'^2 + r't'',$$
$$r_{sss} = r'''t'^3 + \{r', r''\},$$

where $\{r', r''\}$ is a linear combination of the vectors r' and r''. If we substitute the expressions for r_s, r_{ss}, and r_{sss} just found into the formula for k_2 and note that $t'^2 = 1/r'^2$, we obtain

$$k_2 = - (r'r''r''')/(r' \times r'')^2.$$

In concluding this section we shall find all the curves for which the torsion vanishes at every point. We have $k_2 = b' \cdot n = 0$, but as we saw, $b' \cdot \tau = 0$ and $b' \cdot b = 0$. Consequently, $b' = 0$, $b = b_0 \doteq$ constant vector.

The vectors τ and b are perpendicular. Therefore $r' \cdot b_0 = 0$. It follows that $(r(s) - r_0) \cdot b_0 = 0$, which means that the curve lies in the plane given by the vector equation $(r - r_0) \cdot b_0 = 0$.

Thus, as curve whose torsion vanishes at every point is a plane curve. The converse assertion is also true.

§ 5. The Frenet formulas. Natural equations of a curve.

Three half-lines, emanating from a point on the curve and having the directions of the vectors τ, n, b are edges of a trihedron. This trihedron is called the *natural trihedron*.

In order to investigate the properties of the curve in a neighborhood of an arbitrary point P it turns out in many cases to be convenient to choose a cartesian system of coordinates taking the point P on the curve as the origin of coordinates and the edges of the natural trihedron as the coordinate axes. Below we shall obtain the equation of a curve with such a choice of coordinate system.

We shall now express the derivatives of the vectors τ, n, b with respect to arc length of the curve again in terms of τ, n, b. We have

$$\tau' = r'' = k_1 n.$$

To obtain b', let us recall that the vector b' is parallel to n and that $b' \cdot n = k_2$. It follows that

$$b' = k_2 n.$$

Finally,

$$n' = (b \times \tau)' = b' \times \tau + b \times \tau' = k_2 n \times \tau + k_1 b \times n = - (k_1 \tau + k_2 b).$$

The system of equations

$$\tau' = k_1 n,$$
$$n' = - k_1 \tau - k_2 b,$$
$$b' = k_2 n$$

are called the Frenet formulas.

We shall find the expansion of the radius vector $r(s + \Delta s)$ in a neighborhood of an arbitrary P, corresponding to the arc s along the axes of the natural trihedron at this point. We have

$$r(s + \Delta s) = r(s) + \Delta s r'(s) + \frac{\Delta s^2}{2} r''(s) + \frac{\Delta s^3}{6} r'''(s) + \cdots.$$

But at the point P, $r=0$, $r'=\tau$, $r''=k_1 n$, $r'''=k_1' n - k_1^2 \tau - k_1 k_2 b$, and so on. Thus,

$$r(s + \Delta s) = \left(\Delta s - \frac{k_1^2 \Delta s^3}{6} + \cdots \right) \tau +$$

$$\left(\frac{k_1 \Delta s^2}{2} + \frac{k_1' \Delta s^3}{6} + \cdots \right) n +$$

$$\left(- \frac{k_1 k_2 \Delta s^3}{6} + \cdots \right) b.$$

We see that in order to expand the function $r(s + \Delta s)$ as a power series in Δs it is sufficient to know the curvature and torsion of the curve as functions of the arc s. This gives the basis for assuming that the curvature and torsion determine the curve to some extent. And indeed we do have the following valid theorem.

THEOREM. *Suppose $k_1(s)$ and $k_2(s)$ are arbitrary regular functions with $k_1(s) > 0$. Then there exists a unique (up to position in space) curve for which $k_1(s)$ is the curvature and $k_2(s)$ is the torsion at the point corresponding to the arc s.*

PROOF. Let us consider the following system of differential equations

$$\xi' = k_1 \eta,$$
$$\eta' = - k_1 \xi - k_2 \zeta,$$
$$\zeta' = k_2 \eta,$$

where ξ, η, ζ are unknown vector functions.

Suppose $\xi(s)$, $\eta(s)$, $\zeta(s)$ is the solution of this system satisfying the initial conditions $\xi = \xi_0$, $\eta = \eta_0$, $\zeta = \zeta_0$ for $s = s_0$, where ξ_0, η_0, ζ_0 are three mutually perpendicular unit vectors whose triple product equals $1 : (\xi_0, \eta_0, \zeta_0) = 1$.

We shall show that the vectors $\xi(s)$, $\eta(s)$, $\zeta(s)$ are unique and mutually perpendicular for arbitrary s and $(\xi, \eta, \zeta) = 1$. To this end, we shall compute $(\xi^2)'$, $(\eta^2)'$, $(\zeta^2)'$, $(\xi \cdot \eta)'$, $(\eta \cdot \zeta)'$, $(\zeta \cdot \xi)'$. Making use of the equations of the system, we obtain the following expressions for these derivatives:

$$(\xi^2)' = 2k_1\xi \cdot \eta, \quad (\xi \cdot \eta)' = k_1\eta^2 - k_1\xi^2 - k_2\xi \cdot \zeta,$$
$$(\eta^2)' = - k_1\xi \cdot \eta - k_2\eta \cdot \zeta, \quad (\eta \cdot \zeta)' = k_2\eta^2 - k_2\zeta^2 - k_1\xi \cdot \zeta,$$
$$(\zeta^2)' = 2k_2\eta \cdot \zeta, \quad (\zeta \cdot \xi)' = k_1\eta \cdot \zeta + k_2\xi \cdot \eta.$$

If we consider these equations as a system of differential equations for ξ^2, η^2, ζ^2, $\xi \cdot \eta$, $\eta \cdot \zeta$, $\zeta \cdot \xi$, we note that it is satisfied by the set of values $\xi^2 = 1$, $\eta^2 = 1$, $\zeta^2 = 1$, $\xi \cdot \eta = 0$, $\eta \cdot \zeta = 0$, $\zeta \cdot \xi = 0$. On the other hand, this system is satisfied by the values $\xi^2 = \xi^2(s)$, $\eta^2 = \eta^2(s)$, $\cdots$, $\zeta \cdot \xi = \zeta(s) \cdot \xi(s)$. Both these solutions coincide for $s = s_0$, and consequently, they coincide identically according to the theorem on the uniqueness of the solution. Hence, for all s we have

$$\xi^2(s) = 1, \quad \eta^2(s) = 1, \quad \cdots, \quad \zeta(s) \cdot \xi(s) = 0.$$

We shall show that $(\xi(s), \eta(s), \zeta(s)) = 1$. Since ξ, η, ζ are mutually perpendicular unit vectors, we have $(\xi, \eta, \zeta) = \pm 1$. The triple product (ξ, η, ζ) depends continuously on s, it equals $+ 1$ when $s = s_0$, and therefore it is equal to 1 for all s.

We shall now consider the curve γ, defined by the vector equation

$$r = \int_{s_0}^{s} \xi(s)ds.$$

We note first of all that the parametrization of the curve γ is the natural parametrization. In fact, the arc length of the segment s_0s of the curve γ equals

$$\int_{s_0}^{s} |r'(s)|ds = \int_{s_0}^{s} |\xi(s)|ds = s - s_0.$$

The curvature of the curve γ equals $|r''(s)| = |\xi'(s)| = k_1(s)$. The torsion of the curve γ equals

$$- \frac{(r'r''r''')}{k_1^2} = - \frac{(\xi, k_1\eta, k_1'\eta + k_1\eta')}{k_1^2} =$$

$$- \frac{(\xi, k_1\eta, k_1'\eta + k_1(- k_1\xi - k_2\zeta))}{k_1^2} = k_2(s).$$

Thus, the curve γ has curvature $k_1(s)$ and torsion $k_2(s)$ at the point corresponding to the arc s.

This completes the first part of the theorem. We now proceed to the proof of the second part.

Suppose γ_1 and γ_2 are two curves which have the same curvature $k_1(s)$ and torsion $k_2(s)$ at the points corresponding to the arc s. We shall correspond the curves γ_1 and γ_2 by means of points corresponding to the arc s_0, and with the natural trihedra at these points. Suppose τ_1, n_1, b_1 and τ_2, n_2, b_2 are unit tangent, principal normal, and binormal vectors to the curves γ_1 and γ_2 respectively.

The triples of vector functions $\tau_1(s)$, $n_1(s)$, $b_1(s)$ and $\tau_2(s)$, $n_2(s)$, $b_2(s)$ are solutions of the system of equations for ξ, η, ζ. The initial values of these solutions coincide. It follows from this that the solutions coincide identically. In particular, $\tau_1(s) \equiv \tau_2(s)$, or $r_1'(s) \equiv r_2'(s)$. Integrating this equality between the limits s_0, s, we obtain

$$r_1(s) \equiv r_2(s).$$

Thus, the curve γ_2 differs from γ_1 only by its position in space.
This completes the proof of the theorem.
The system of equations

$$k_1 = k_1(s), \quad k_2 = k_2(s)$$

are called the *natural equations* of the curve. According to the theorem proved above, a curve is defined uniquely to within position in space by its natural equations.

§ 6. Plane curves. In this section we shall consider the osculating circle, evolutes, and involutes of a plane curve.

Suppose γ is a plane curve and that P is a point on γ. A circumference κ passing through the point P, is called the osculating circle to the curve γ at the point P if the curve has, at this point, contact of the second order with the circle. The center of the osculating circle is called the center of curvature of the curve.

We shall find the osculating circle of a regular curve γ at a point P, where the curvature is different from zero. Suppose $r = r(s)$ is the natural parametrization of the curve. The equation of any circumference has the form

$$(r - a)^2 - R^2 = 0,$$

where a is the position vector of the center of the circumference and R is its radius.

According to the theorem in § 4, Chapter II, a necessary and sufficient condition that the curve γ have contact of the second order with the circumference at the point P is that the following conditions be satisfied at this point:

$$(r(s) - a)^2 - R^2 = 0,$$

$$\frac{d}{ds}\{(r(s) - a)^2 - R^2\} = 2(r(s) - a)\cdot r'(s) = 0$$

$$\frac{d^2}{ds^2}\{(r(s) - a)^2 - R^2\} = 2r'^2 + 2(r(s) - a)\cdot r''(s) = 0.$$

Of these three conditions, the first expresses the fact that the point P lies on the circumference. It is clear from the second condition that the vector $(r(s) - a)$, directed from the center of the circle at the point P, is perpendicular to the tangent to the curve; this means that the center of the circle lies on the normal to the curve. The third condition defines the radius of the circle. In fact, $r'^2(s) = 1$, $r''(s) = kn$ and since $|r(s) - a|$ is the radius R of the circle at the point P, and the vector $r(s) - a$ is parallel to the vector n, we have $1 - Rk = 0$. Thus, the radius of the osculating circle equals the radius of curvature of the curve. It follows from this that if the curvature at the point P equals zero, the osculating circle to the curve does not exist at the point P. In this case, the circle degenerates into a straight line, and the tangent to the curve has contact of the second order with the curve.

We have thus found the radius and the position of the center of the osculating circle. We shall now define the *evolute* of a curve.

The evolute of a curve is the geometric locus of the centers of curvature of the curve.

We shall find the equation of the evolute of a regular curve γ. Suppose $r = r(s)$ is the natural parametrization of the curve. Then the radius vector of the center of curvature of the curve is

$$\tilde{r} = r + (1/k)n.$$

Suppose $x = x(t)$, $y = y(t)$ is any regular parametrization of the curve γ.

We have

$$\tilde{x} = x + (1/k)\xi, \quad \tilde{y} = y + (1/k)\eta,$$

where ξ, η are the projections of the vector n onto the coordinate axes. But

$$1/k - \pm \frac{(x'^2 + y'^2)^{3/2}}{y''x' - x''y'} \, , \quad \xi - \mp \frac{y'}{(x'^2 + y'^2)^{1/2}} \, , \quad \eta = + \frac{x'}{(x'^2 + y'^2)^{1/2}} \, .$$

It follows that the equations of the evolute are

$$\tilde{x} = x - y' \frac{x'^2 + y'^2}{y''x' - x''y'} \, , \quad \tilde{y} = y + x' \frac{x'^2 + y'^2}{y''x' - x''y'} \, .$$

We shall explain what the evolute of a curve represents. We shall limit ourselves to the consideration of the following fundamental cases:

a) $k'(s) > 0$ or $k'(s) < 0$, and $k(s)$ does not vanish, along the entire curve;

b) $k'(s) > 0$ or $k'(s) < 0$ along the entire curve, and $k(s)$ is zero for $s = s_0$;

c) $k'(s) > 0$ for $s < s_0$, $k'(s) < 0$ for $s > s_0$, $k'(s_0) = 0$, $k''(s_0) \neq 0$, and $k(s)$ does not vanish.

In the first case, the evolute is a regular curve without singular points (Fig. 11a). In fact, in this case we have

$$\tilde{r}' = (r + n/k)' = \tau + \left(-\frac{\tau k}{k} + n \left(\frac{1}{k} \right)' \right) = -\frac{k'n}{k^2} \neq 0.$$

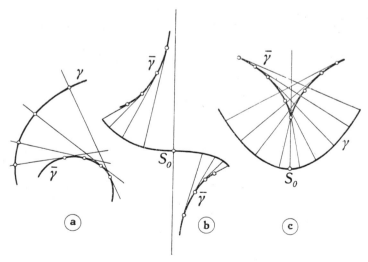

Fig. 11

In the second case, the evolute decomposes into two regular curves, which are the evolutes of the parts of the curve γ corresponding to $s < s_0$ and $s > s_0$, respectively (see Fig. 11b).

In the third case, the evolute is a regular curve, the point on the evolute corresponding to the point s_0 on the curve is a singular point, namely a turning point of the first kind (see Fig. 11c). We shall show this.

For $s = s_0$, we have

$$\tilde{r}' = n(1/k)' = 0, \quad \tilde{r}'' = - k\tau(1/k)' + n(1/k)'',$$
$$\tilde{r}''' = - 2k\tau(1/k)'' + n(1/k)'''.$$

We shall refer the evolute to a rectangular coordinate system, taking the point $\tilde{Q}(s_0)$ on the evolute as the origin of coordinates, and the tangent and normal of the curve γ at the point $Q(s_0)$ as the direction of the x and y axes. For such a choice of coordinate system, we shall have

$$\tilde{x} = (- k/3)(1/k)''(s - s_0)^3 + \cdots$$
$$\tilde{y} = \tfrac{1}{2}(1/k)''(s - s_0)^2 + \cdots.$$

It follows from this that the point $\tilde{Q}(s_0)$ on the evolute is a singular point, namely a turning point of the first kind.

We shall now consider some properties of the evolute.

Suppose γ is a regular curve for which $k'(s)$ retains the same sign throughout, and $k(s)$ never vanishes. In this case, as we showed, the evolute $\tilde{\gamma}$ of the curve γ is a regular curve without singular points.

We shall find the arc length of the segment of the evolute, corresponding to the segment $s_1 s_2$ on the curve. We have

$$\tilde{s}(s_1, s_2) = \int_{s_1}^{s_2} |\tilde{r}'| ds = \int_{s_1}^{s_2} |(1/k)'| ds.$$

It follows that

$$\tilde{s}(s_1, s_2) = \left| \frac{1}{k(s_2)} - \frac{1}{k(s_1)} \right|$$

since k' retains the same sign.

Thus, the arc length of a segment of the evolute equals the absolute value of the difference of the radii of curvature at the points corresponding to the endpoints of this segment.

We shall show that the evolute $\tilde{\gamma}$ is the envelope of the normals to the curve γ. In fact, the point $\tilde{Q}(s)$ on the evolute lies on the normal to the curve at the point $Q(s)$. The tangent to the evolute at the point $\tilde{Q}(s)$ has the direction $\tilde{r}' = n(1/k)'$, and consequently, it coincides with the normal to the curve at the point $Q(s)$.

We shall now define an *involute* of a curve.

Suppose γ is a regular curve and that $r = r(s)$ is its natural parametrization. Suppose $Q(s_0)$ is any point on the curve. We mark off on the tangent to the curve γ at an arbitrary point $Q(s)$, $s < s_0$, a segment equal to $s_0 - s$, in the direction of the vector $\tau(s)$. We denote the point thus obtained by $\bar{Q}(s)$ (see Fig. 12).

The geometric locus of the points $\bar{Q}(s)$ is called an involute of the curve.

Obviously, a curve has an infinite number of involutes.

A graphic representation of an involute can be gotten in the following way. We imagine a taut string, wound on the part of the curve γ, corresponding to $s < s_0$ with endpoint at the point $Q(s_0)$. If this string is unwound by its end, tangentially to the curve, then its endpoint will describe an involute of the curve.

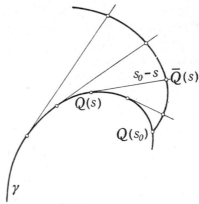

Fig. 12

We shall now find the equation of the involute. By definition, the position vector of the point $\bar{Q}(s)$ on the involute is

$$\bar{r} = r + (s_0 - s)\tau.$$

This is therefore the equation of the involute.

In the case of an arbitrary parametrization $r = r(t)$, the equation of the involute will obviously be

$$\bar{r} = r + \frac{r'}{\sqrt{r'^2}} \int_t^{t_0} \sqrt{r'^2}\, dt.$$

We shall explain what the involute represents in two fundamental cases:

a) $k(s)$ does not vanish for all $s < s_0$ on the curve;

b) $k(s)$ vanishes only for $s = s_1$, where $k'(s_1) \neq 0$.

In the first case, an involute is a regular curve without singularities. In fact,

$$\bar{r}' = (r - (s - s_0)\tau)' = -(s - s_0)kn \neq 0.$$

In the second case, an involute is also a regular curve, but the point $\bar{Q}(s_1)$ on the involute is a singular point, namely a turning point of the second kind. In order to prove this assertion, we must refer the involute to a rectangular cartesian coordinate system taking the point $\bar{Q}(s_1)$ as the origin of coordinates, and as its coordinate axes, straight lines parallel to the tangent and normal to the curve γ at the point $Q(s_1)$.

We shall consider some properties of an involute.

Suppose γ is a regular curve with nonzero curvature and let $\bar{\gamma}$ be one of its involutes.

The tangent to the involute $\bar{\gamma}$ at the point $\bar{Q}(s)$ has the direction $\bar{r}' = (s - s_0)kn$, i.e. it is parallel to the normal to the curve γ at the point $Q(s)$. Since the point $\bar{Q}(s)$ lies on the tangent to the curve γ at the point $Q(s)$, the normal to the involute at the point $\bar{Q}(s)$ is the tangent to the curve at the point $Q(s)$.

The curve γ is the evolute of its involute. To prove this, it suffices to show that the point $Q(s)$ on the curve γ is the center of curvature of the involute at the point $\bar{Q}(s)$. In fact, the point $Q(s)$ lies on the normal to the involute at the point $\bar{Q}(s)$. The radius of curvature of the involute at this point is

$$1/\bar{k} = \frac{(\bar{r}'^2)^{3/2}}{\sqrt{r''^2 r'^2 - (r' \cdot r'')^2}} = s_0 - s.$$

It follows from this that the point $Q(s)$ is the center of curvature of the involute at the point $\bar{Q}(s)$.

EXERCISES FOR CHAPTER III

1. Find the length of the segment $-a \leq x \leq a$ of the parabola $y = bx^2$.

ANSWER: $s = \dfrac{2ab\sqrt{1 + 4a^2b^2} + \ln(2ab + \sqrt{1 + 4a^2b^2})}{2a}$.

2. Find the length of the segment of the curve

$$x = a \cosh t, \quad y = a \sinh t, \quad z = at$$

between the points 0 and t.

ANSWER: $s = \sqrt{2}a \sinh t$.

3. Find the arc length of the astroid

$$x = a \cos^3 t, \quad y = a \sin^3 t.$$

ANSWER: $s = 6a$.

4. Find the length of the segment $0 \le t \le 2\pi$ of the cycloid

$$x = a(t - \sin t), \quad y = a(1 - \cos t).$$

ANSWER: $s = 8a$.

5. Find the expression for arc length of the curve defined by an equation in polar coordinates

$$\rho = \rho(\vartheta).$$

ANSWER: $s(\vartheta_1, \vartheta_2) = \int_{\vartheta_1}^{\vartheta_2} \sqrt{\rho^2 + \rho'^2} \, d\vartheta$.

6. Find the curvature of the curve

$$x = t - \sin t, \quad y = 1 - \cos t, \quad z = 4 \sin \frac{t}{2}.$$

ANSWER: $k_1 = \frac{1}{4} \sqrt{1 + \sin^2 \frac{t}{2}}$.

7. Find the curvature at the point $(0, 0, 0)$ of the curve defined by the equations in the implicit form

$$x + \sinh x = \sin y + y,$$
$$z + e^z = x + \ln(1 + x) + 1.$$

ANSWER: $k_1 = \sqrt{6}/9$.

8. Find the curvature and torsion at an arbitrary point t of the curve given in Exercise 2.

ANSWER: $k_1 = 1/(2a \cosh^2 t)$, $k_2 = 1/(2a \cosh^2 t)$.

9. Compute the torsion of the curve

$$x = a \cosh t \cos t, \quad y = a \cosh t \sin t, \quad z = at.$$

ANSWER: $k_2 = -a \cosh t$.

10. Show that the curvature and torsion of a simple helix are constant.

11. Find the expression for the curvature of a plane curve given in the polar form.

ANSWER: $k_1 = \left(\dfrac{1}{\rho} + \left(\dfrac{1}{\rho}\right)''\right) \Big/ \left(1 + \left(\dfrac{1}{\rho}\right)'^2\right)^{3/2}$.

12. Show that the torsion of the curve

$$r = a \int b(t) \times b'(t)\,dt,$$

where $b(t)$ is a vector function satisfying the conditions $|b(t)| = 1$, $b'(t) \neq 0$, is constant.

13. Show that the ratio of the curvature to the torsion of the curve

$$x = a \int \sin \alpha(t)\,dt, \quad y = a \int \cos \alpha(t)\,dt, \quad z = bt$$

is constant.

14. Find the evolute of the parabola $y^2 = 2px$.

ANSWER: Semicubical parabola

$$27py^2 = 8(x - p)^3.$$

15. Find the evolute of the tractrix

$$x = -a\left(\ln \tan \frac{t}{2} + \cos t\right), \quad y = a \sin t.$$

ANSWER: Catenary

$$y = a \cosh \frac{x}{a}.$$

16. Find the evolute of the astroid

$$|x|^{\frac{2}{3}} + |y|^{\frac{2}{3}} = 1.$$

ANSWER: Astroid

$$|x + y|^{\frac{2}{3}} + |x - y|^{\frac{2}{3}} = 2.$$

17. Find the evolute of the circle $x^2 + y^2 = R^2$.

ANSWER: $x = R(\cos \vartheta + (\vartheta - c) \sin \vartheta)$,
$y = R(\sin \vartheta - (\vartheta - c) \cos \vartheta)$.

18. Find all the plane curves with given natural equation $k = k(s)$.

ANSWER: $x = \int \sin \alpha(s)\,ds$, $y = \int \cos \alpha(s)\,ds$, where $\alpha(s) = \int k(s)\,ds$.

PROBLEMS AND THEOREMS FOR CHAPTER III

1. A function $f(t)$ defined on the interval $a < t < b$ is said to be a function of bounded variation if the sum

$$\Sigma_k |f(t_k) - f(t_{k-1})|$$

is uniformly bounded for arbitrary t_1, t_2, $\cdots$, t_n such that $a < t_1 < t_2 < \cdots < t_n < b$.

Prove that a curve γ is rectifiable if and only if it permits the parametrization

$$x = x(t), \quad y = y(t), \quad z = z(t),$$

where $x(t), y(t), z(t)$ are functions of bounded variation, in a neighborhood of each of its points.

2. Prove that if a curve possesses any one of the following properties then it has the remaining three properties also:
   1) the tangents to the curve form a constant angle with some direction,
   2) the binormals to the curve form a constant angle with some direction,
   3) the principal normals to the curve are parallel to some plane,
   4) the ratio of the curvature to the torsion of the curve is constant.

Find the general form of the curve which has these properties.

3. Prove that if the curvature and torsion of the curve are constant and different from zero then this curve is a simple helix.

4. Prove that if a one-to-one correspondence is established between the points of two curves for which the binormals to the curves coincide in corresponding points, then the curves are plane curves.

5. Prove that an arbitrary curve with constant torsion and nonzero curvature can be given by the vector equation

$$r = c \int b(t) \times b'(t)dt,$$

where $b(t)$ is a vector function satisfying the conditions

$$|b(t)| = 1, \quad b'(t) \neq 0.$$

6. Construct the curve if one of the three vector functions $\tau(s)$, $n(s)$ and $b(s)$ is given.

7. If a correspondence between the points of two curves can be

established in such a way that the tangents at corresponding points of these curves are parallel then the principal normals and binormals are also parallel. Prove this.

8_1. The curves γ_1 and γ_2 are said to be Bertrand curves if a one-to-one point correspondence can be established between them for which the principal normals coincide at corresponding points.

Prove the following properties of the curves γ_1, γ_2:

a) the distance between corresponding points on the curves γ_1 and γ_2 is constant;

b) the tangents to the curves γ_1 and γ_2 at corresponding points form a constant angle;

c) the curvature and torsion of each of these curves are connected by the relation

$$a \sin \vartheta k_1 + a \cos \vartheta k_2 = \sin \vartheta,$$

where a is the distance between corresponding points on the curves γ_1, γ_2 and ϑ is the angle between the tangents at the corresponding points.

8_2. Prove that if the curvature and torsion of a curve are connected by the linear relationship

$$a \sin \vartheta k_1 + a \cos \vartheta k_2 = \sin \vartheta,$$

then the curve is a Bertrand curve.

8_3. Prove that a curve defined by the vector equation

$$r = a \int e(t) dt + b \int e(t) \times e'(t) dt,$$

where $e(t)$ is a vector function, satisfying the conditions $|e(t)| = 1$, $|e'(t)| = 1$, is a Bertrand curve. And conversely, an arbitrary Bertrand curve can be defined by a vector equation of this type.

PART TWO

THEORY OF SURFACES

CHAPTER IV

CONCEPT OF SURFACE

§ 1. Elementary surface. Simple surface. General surface.
A plane region is said to be an *elementary* region if it is the image of
an open circle (i.e. the interior of a circle) under a one-to-one and
bicontinuous mapping. Briefly, this is expressed as follows: an
elementary region is a region homeomorphic with a circle.

Suppose γ is a simple closed curve in the plane. The well-known
Jordan theorem states that a simple closed curve decomposes the
plane into two regions and is the frontier of each of these regions.
One of these regions is finite and the other is infinite. It turns out
that the finite region is homeomorphic to a circle. Thus, the interior of a square, rectangle, ellipse are all elementary regions.

We now define an elementary surface.

A set Φ of points in space will be called an *elementary surface* if it
is the image of an elementary region in a plane under a one-to-one
and bicontinuous mapping of this region into space.

Suppose Φ is an elementary surface and G is an elementary plane
region whose image under a one-to-one and bicontinuous mapping f
is the surface Φ. Let u and v be the cartesian coordinates of an
arbitrary point belonging to the region G and let x, y, z be the
coordinates of the corresponding point on the surface. The coordinates x, y, z of the point on the surface are functions of the coordinates of the point in the region G:

$$x = f_1(u, v), \quad y = f_2(u, v), \quad z = f_3(u, v).$$

This system of equations, which determine the mapping f of the
region G into space, are called the *equations* of the surface in the
parametric form.

A set Φ of points in space will be called a *simple surface* if this set is connected and every point X in Φ has a neighborhood G such that the subset of Φ which lies in G is an elementary surface.

An elementary surface is a simple surface. But the set of elementary surfaces forms only a part of the set of all simple surfaces. For example, the sphere is a simple surface but it is not elementary.

Simple surfaces cannot be characterized generally and simply in the large as this was done for simple curves. Some idea of the variety of simple surfaces is given by the following reasoning. If an arbitrary closed set of points is deleted from any simple surface in such a way that the connectivity of the remaining part is left undisturbed, then the remaining part will also be a simple surface.

A simple surface is said to be complete if the limit point of any convergent sequence of points on the surface also is a point on the surface. For example, a sphere and a paraboloid are complete surfaces, but a spherical segment is not a complete surface (we have in mind here a spherical segment without the circumference bounding it).

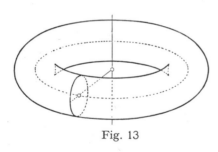

Fig. 13

If a simple complete surface is finite, then it is said to be closed. Besides spheres, the surface of a torus, obtained by revolving a circumference about a straight line lying in the plane of the circumference and not intersecting it (Fig. 13), is for example, also a closed surface.

We now define the concept of *neighborhood* of a point on a simple surface.

A neighborhood of a point X on a simple surface Φ is the common part of the surface Φ and some neighborhood of the point X in space. In agreement with the definition, each point of the simple surface has a neighborhood which is an elementary surface. In the sequel, in speaking of a neighborhood of a point on a surface we shall have in mind such an elementary neighborhood.

A set Φ of points in space will be called a *general surface* if it is the image of a simple surface under a continuous and locally one-to-one mapping of it into space.

We shall say that the mapping f_1 of a simple surface Φ_1 and the mapping f_2 of the simple surface Φ_2 define the same general surface

Φ if a one-to-one and bicontinuous correspondence can be established between the points of the surfaces Φ_1 and Φ_2 for which the images of corresponding points of these surfaces coincide on the surface Φ.

Suppose the general surface Φ is the image under a one-to-one and continuous mapping into space of a simple surface $\bar{\Phi}$. We shall say that a sequence of points $f(X_n)$ on the surface Φ *converges* to the point $f(X)$ if the sequence of points X_n on the simple surface $\bar{\Phi}$ converges to the point X. A neighborhood of the point $f(X)$ on the surface Φ is the image of an arbitrary neighborhood of the point X on the surface $\bar{\Phi}$ under the mapping f.

Although the convergence of sequences of points on a general surface Φ and the neighborhoods of points on Φ are defined as the images of convergent sequences and neighborhoods on a simple surface, starting with some definite mapping, these concepts do not depend on the particular character of the mapping f in the sense that starting with another mapping f' of another simple surface which defines the same general surface Φ, we arrive at the same convergent sequences and the same neighborhoods of points on the surface Φ. This follows from the possibility of establishing a one-to-one and bicontinuous correspondence between the points on the simple surfaces $\bar{\Phi}$ and $\bar{\Phi}'$ for which the images of corresponding points on these surfaces under the mappings f and f' coincide. The images of the corresponding convergent sequences on the surfaces $\bar{\Phi}$ and $\bar{\Phi}'$ define the same convergent sequence on the surface Φ. The images of corresponding neighborhoods of corresponding points on the surfaces $\bar{\Phi}$ and $\bar{\Phi}'$ define the same neighborhood of the point on the general surface Φ.

In conclusion, we note that if a simple surface, in particular an elementary surface, is considered as a general surface, then the concept of convergence of points on it is equivalent to the concept of geometric convergence, and the concept of neighborhood is equivalent to the concept of geometric neighborhood introduced for simple surfaces.

§ 2. Regular surface. Analytic definition of a surface. It

follows from the definition of a general surface that there exists a neighborhood for each of its points which is an elementary surface.

A surface Φ will be said to be *regular* (k-times differentiable) if each of the points on this surface has a neighborhood, permitting a

regular parametrization, i.e. allowing one to write the equations in
the parametric form

$$x = f_1(u, v), \quad y = f_2(u, v), \quad z = f_3(u, v),$$

where f_1, f_2, f_3 are regular (k-times continuously differentiable)
functions, defined in an elementary region G of the u, v-plane. For
$k = 1$, the surface is said to be *smooth*.

A surface is said to be *analytic* if it allows an analytic parametrization (the functions f_1, f_2, f_3 are analytic) in a sufficiently
small neighborhood of each of its points.

In the sequel we shall consider regular surfaces exclusively.

A point P on a regular surface will be called a *regular point* if the
surface permits a regular parametrization in a neighborhood of this
point

$$x = x(u, v), \quad y = y(u, v), \quad z = z(u, v),$$

satisfying the condition that the rank of the matrix

$$\begin{pmatrix} x_u & y_u & z_u \\ x_v & y_v & z_v \end{pmatrix}$$

evaluated at the point P equals two. In the contrary case a point of
the surface is called a *singular point*.

Thus, if a point P of a regular surface is singular then the rank of
the above-indicated matrix is less than two for any regular parametrization of Φ in a neighborhood of the point P.

A curve on a surface all points of which are singular points of the
surface is called a *singular curve*.

In the sequel, if the contrary is not expressly stated, we shall
assume that all points on the surface considered are regular points.

In agreement with the definition, in the neighborhood of each of
its points a regular surface can be given by means of equations in the
parametric form

$$x = x(u, v), \quad y = y(u, v), \quad z = z(u, v),$$

where $x(u, v)$, $y(u, v)$, $z(u, v)$ are regular functions of the variables
u, v defined in some region G of the u, v-plane. The question
naturally arises, when does the system of equations

$$x = x(u, v), \quad y = y(u, v), \quad z = z(u, v),$$

where $x(u, v)$, $y(u, v)$, $z(u, v)$ are regular functions in some region G

of the u, v-plane, define a surface? The answer to this question is given, in many cases, by the following theorem.

THEOREM. *If $x(u, v)$, $y(u, v)$, $z(u, v)$ are regular functions in the region G of the u, v-plane which satisfy the condition that the rank of the matrix*

$$\begin{pmatrix} x_u & y_u & z_u \\ x_v & y_v & z_v \end{pmatrix}$$

equals two everywhere in G, then the system of equations

$$x = x(u, v), \quad y = y(u, v), \quad z = z(u, v)$$

defines some surface Φ. This surface is the image of a simple surface G under a continuous and locally one-to-one mapping which assigns to the point (u, v) in the region G a point in space with coordinates $x(u, v)$, $y(u, v)$, $z(u, v)$.

In the proof of the necessity part of this theorem, we obviously need only the assertion about the local one-to-oneness of the indicated mapping. We shall prove this.

We assume that the assertion is not true; then there exists a point (u_0, v_0) in the region G which is such that in every neighborhood, however small, of this point, one can find two distinct points (u_1, v_1) and (u_2, v_2) such that

$$x(u_1, v_1) - x(u_2, v_2) = 0, \quad y(u_1, v_1) - y(u_2, v_2) = 0,$$
$$z(u_1, v_1) - z(u_2, v_2) = 0.$$

We have

$$x(u_1, v_1) - x(u_2, v_2) = (x(u_1, v_1) - x(u_1, v_2)) + (x(u_1, v_2) - x(u_2, v_2)) =$$
$$(v_1 - v_2)x_v(u_1, \vartheta_1) + (u_1 - u_2)x_u(\vartheta_1', v_2) = 0.$$

Analogously

$$y(u_1, v_1) - y(u_2, v_2) = (v_1 - v_2)y_v(u_1, \vartheta_2) + (u_1 - u_2)y_u(\vartheta_2', v_2) = 0,$$
$$z(u_1, v_1) - z(u_2, v_2) = (v_1 - v_2)z_v(u_1, \vartheta_3) + (u_1 - u_2)z_u(\vartheta_3', v_2) = 0.$$

Considering the fact that $u_1 - u_2$, $v_1 - v_2$ do not vanish simultaneously, we conclude from the three equations thus obtained that the rank of the matrix

$$\begin{pmatrix} x_u(u_1, \vartheta_1'), & y_u(u_1, \vartheta_2'), & z_u(u_1, \vartheta_3') \\ x_v(\vartheta_1, v_2), & y_v(\vartheta_2, v_2), & z_v(\vartheta_3, v_2) \end{pmatrix}$$

is less than two, i.e. its second order determinants are equal to zero. In virtue of the continuity of the functions x_u, x_v, $\cdots$, z_v it follows from this that all the second order determinants of the matrix

$$\begin{pmatrix} x_u & y_u & z_u \\ x_v & y_v & z_v \end{pmatrix}$$

are equal to zero at the point (u_0, v_0), i.e. the rank of the matrix is less than two. We have thus arrived at a contradiction. This concludes the proof of the assertion.

With a proper choice of x, y, z-coordinates axes, some simple surfaces permit a parametrization for the entire surface of the form

$$x = u, \quad y = v, \quad z = f(u, v),$$

where $f(u, v)$ is a function defined in a region G of the u, v-plane. The equations of this surface can be written in the equivalent form

$$z = f(x, y).$$

Such a parametrization of the surface differs from others by its greater graphicalness. The correspondence between points on the surface and points of the region in the x, y-plane is realized by a projection by straight lines, parallel to the z-axis.

We now go over to the implicit definition of a surface.

We shall say that the surface Φ is defined by the equation

$$\varphi(x, y, z) = 0,$$

expressing by this only the fact that the coordinates of points on the surface satisfy the given equation. In this connection, there may exist points in space which satisfy the given equation and which do not belong to the surface Φ.

Thus, defining a surface by an equation in the implicit form $\varphi(x, y, z) = 0$ is incomplete, in contrast to the parametric representation considered above. Nonetheless, some problems concerning surfaces can be solved even if we have at our disposal only such an incomplete definition of the surface.

The following theorem plays an important role in the investigation of surfaces defined by the equation $\varphi(x, y, z) = 0$.

THEOREM. *Suppose $\varphi(x, y, z)=0$ is a regular function of the variables x, y, z. Suppose M is the set of points in space satisfying the equation $\varphi(x, y, z) = 0$, and that (x_0, y_0, x_0) is a point in M for which $\varphi_x^2 + \varphi_y^2 + \varphi_z^2 \neq 0$. Then the point (x_0, y_0, z_0) has a neighborhood such that all the points of the set M belonging to this neighborhood form a regular elementary surface.*

PROOF. Suppose for definiteness that $\varphi_z \neq 0$ at the point (x_0, y_0, z_0). By the implicit function theorem there exist positive numbers δ and ε and a regular function $\psi(x, y)$, defined in the region $|x - x_0| < \delta$, $|y - y_0| < \delta$, such that all the points $(x, y, \psi(x, y))$, $|x - x_0| < \delta$, $|y - y_0| < \delta$ satisfy the equation $\varphi(x, y, z) = 0$ where these points exhaust the set of all points in the parallelepiped $|x - x_0| < \delta$, $|y - y_0| < \delta$, $|z - z_0| < \varepsilon$, satisfying the equation $\varphi(x, y, z) = 0$. The elementary surface, referred to in the theorem, is given by the equation

$$z = \psi(x, y), \quad |x - x_0| < \delta, \quad |y - y_0| < \delta.$$

This completes the proof of the theorem.

§ 3. **Special parametrizations of a surface.** A regular surface permits an infinite number of parametrizations in a neighborhood of each of its points. In fact, suppose

$$x = x(u, v), \quad y = y(u, v), \quad z = z(u, v)$$

is any parametrization of the surface in a neighborhood of the point $Q(u_0, v_0)$.

If $\varphi(\alpha, \beta)$ and $\psi(\alpha, \beta)$ are arbitrary regular functions satisfying the conditions

$$\begin{aligned} u_0 &= \varphi(\alpha_0, \beta_0), \\ v_0 &= \psi(\alpha_0, \beta_0), \end{aligned} \quad \begin{vmatrix} \varphi_\alpha & \varphi_\beta \\ \psi_\alpha & \psi_\beta \end{vmatrix} \neq 0$$

at the point (α_0, β_0), then the equations

$$x = x(\varphi, \psi), \quad y = y(\varphi, \psi), \quad z = z(\varphi, \psi)$$

also define a regular parametrization of the surface. This follows in an obvious manner from the fact that the formulas

$$u = \varphi(\alpha, \beta), \quad v = \psi(\alpha, \beta)$$

define a one-to-one and bicontinuous mapping of a sufficiently small neighborhood of the point (α_0, β_0) in the α, β-plane onto some neighborhood of the point (u_0, v_0) in the u, v-plane.

In the investigation of regular surfaces, it is convenient to use special parametrizations. We shall consider the special parametrization which is most frequently used.

Suppose

$$x = x(u, v), \quad y = y(u, v), \quad z = z(u, v)$$

is any regular parametrization of a surface in a neighborhood of the point $Q(u_0, v_0)$. Since the rank of the matrix

$$\begin{pmatrix} x_u & y_u & z_u \\ x_v & y_v & z_v \end{pmatrix}$$

equals two, we can, without loss of generality, assume that the determinant

$$\begin{vmatrix} x_u & y_u \\ x_v & y_v \end{vmatrix}$$

does not vanish at the point Q. By the implicit function theorem, the system of equations

$$x = x(u, v), \quad y = y(u, v)$$

is uniquely solvable in a neighborhood of the point Q. More precisely, there exist regular functions $u = \varphi(x, y)$ and $v = \psi(x, y)$ satisfying the equations $x = x(u, v)$ and $y = y(u, v)$ identically in a sufficiently small neighborhood of the point (x_0, y_0), $x_0 = x(u_0, v_0)$, $y_0 = y(u_0, v_0)$, where $\varphi(x_0, y_0) = u_0$, $\psi(x_0, y_0) = v_0$.

From this it follows that our surface permits the parametrization

$$x = \alpha, \quad y = \beta, \quad z = z(\varphi(\alpha, \beta), \quad \psi(\alpha, \beta)) = \bar{z}(\alpha, \beta)$$

in a sufficiently small neighborhood of the point Q, or, what amounts to the same thing, that $z = \bar{z}(x, y)$.

Suppose $x = x(u, v)$, $y = y(u, v)$, $z = z(u, v)$ is any regular parametrization of the surface in a neighborhood of the point $Q(u_0, v_0)$.

Suppose we consider two differential equations

$$A_1(u, v)du + B_1(u, v)dv = 0,$$
$$A_2(u, v)du + B_2(u, v)dv = 0$$

in a neighborhood of the point (u_0, v_0), where the differential equations satisfy the condition

$$\begin{vmatrix} A_1 & B_1 \\ A_2 & B_2 \end{vmatrix} \neq 0$$

at the point (u_0, v_0).

If $\varphi(u, v) = \bar{u} = \text{constant}$ and $\psi(u, v) = \bar{v} = \text{constant}$ is a solution of these differential equations, satisfying the conditions $\varphi_u{}^2 + \varphi_v{}^2 \neq 0$, $\psi_u{}^2 + \psi_v{}^2 \neq 0$ at the point (u_0, v_0), then the surface permits a parametrization

$$x = \bar{x}(\bar{u}, \bar{v}), \quad y = \bar{y}(\bar{u}, \bar{v}), \quad z = \bar{z}(\bar{u}, \bar{v})$$

in a neighborhood of the point O, where

$$\bar{x}(\varphi(u, v), \quad \psi(u, v)) = x(u, v), \quad \bar{y}(\varphi(u, v), \quad \psi(u, v)) = y(u, v),$$
$$\bar{z}(\varphi(u, v), \quad \psi(u, v)) = z(u, v).$$

In order to prove this assertion, it is obviously sufficient to show that

$$\begin{vmatrix} \varphi_u & \varphi_v \\ \psi_u & \psi_v \end{vmatrix} \neq 0$$

at the point (u_0, v_0). In fact, by assumption $\varphi(u, v) = \text{constant}$ is a solution of the first equation, and therefore $\varphi_u du + \varphi_v dv = 0$ must be satisfied identically in virtue of the first equation. It follows that

$$\begin{vmatrix} \varphi_u & \varphi_v \\ A_1 & B_1 \end{vmatrix} = 0.$$

Analogously, we have that

$$\begin{vmatrix} \psi_u & \psi_v \\ A_2 & B_2 \end{vmatrix} = 0.$$

If we assume that $\begin{vmatrix} \varphi_u & \varphi_v \\ \psi_u & \psi_v \end{vmatrix} = 0$, then we easily get

$$\begin{vmatrix} A_1 & B_1 \\ A_2 & B_2 \end{vmatrix} = 0,$$

which is impossible. This completes the proof of the assertion.

§ 4. Singular points on regular surfaces.

In the present section we ought to characterize the singular points on a surface as completely as we did for the singular points on curves. However, since we do not wish to unduly expand this book, we shall not do this. Therefore, we shall limit ourselves to the most general discussions on this point.

Suppose $x = x(u, v)$, $y = y(u, v)$, $z = z(u, v)$ is a regular parametrization of a regular surface.

Suppose the rank of the matrix

$$\begin{pmatrix} x_u & y_u & z_u \\ x_v & y_v & z_v \end{pmatrix}$$

is less than two at the point $Q(u_0, v_0)$ on this surface. The question is, how does one recognize whether or not the point is a singular point on the surface, or whether or not it is a regular point?

We shall give sufficient criteria that the point Q be a singular point.

We shall make use of the vector equation of the surface, $r = r(u, v)$. Then the condition that the rank of the above matrix be less than two is expressed by the fact that the vector product $r_u \times r_v$ vanishes.

Suppose $P(u, v)$ is a point on the surface near Q; suppose that $r_u \times r_v \neq 0$ at this point. We consider the vector function

$$\xi(u, v) = \frac{r_u(u, v) \times r_v(u, v)}{|r_u(u, v) \times r_v(u, v)|}.$$

Then a necessary condition that the point Q be a regular point is that the vector function $\xi(u, v)$ tend to a definite limit as $P \to Q$.

Looking a trifle ahead, we note that $\xi(u, v)$ is the unit normal vector to the surface at the point P. The normal to the surface is defined independently of any concrete parametrization of the surface. If the point Q is a regular point on the surface, then the normal to the surface in a neighborhood of this point depends continuously on the position of the point and, consequently, the unit vector $\xi(u, v)$ tends to a definite limit, the unit normal vector to the surface at the point Q, as $P \to Q$.

Suppose now that $\xi(u, v)$ tends to some unit vector as $P \to Q$. We choose the point $P'(u', v')$, near Q, different from P, on the surface, and we define $\omega(P, P')$ by

$$\omega(P, P') = \frac{(r(u, v) - r(u_0, v_0)) \cdot (r(u', v') - r(u_0, v_0))}{|r(u, v) - r(u_0, v_0)| \, |r(u', v') - r(u_0, v_0)|}.$$

Then the point Q will, as is well known, be a singular point if the greatest lower bound of the expression $\omega(P, P')$ is greater than -1 as $P, P' \to Q$.

We shall show this.

The expression $\omega(P, P')$ has a simple geometric interpretation. It is the cosine of the angle formed by the segments QP and QP' (Fig. 14). We shall assume that the point Q is a regular point and that $r = r(u, v)$ is a parametrization for which $\bar{r}_u \times \bar{r}_v$ is different from 0 at the point Q. We choose the points P and P' in a special way, namely we take them to be $P(\bar{u}_0 + h, \bar{v}_0)$, $P'(\bar{u}_0 - h, \bar{v}_0)$. Then $\omega(P, P') \to -1$ as $h \to 0$. Since the cosine is not less than -1, -1 is the greatest lower bound of the expression $\omega(P, P')$ as $P, P' \to Q$.

Thus, if the greatest lower bound of the expression $\omega(P, P')$ is not equal to -1 as $P, P' \to Q$, then Q is, as known, a singular point.

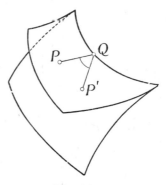

Fig. 14

In conclusion, we shall say a few words about singular points on a surface defined by the equation $\varphi(x, y, z) = 0$.

First of all, only those points where $\varphi_x = \varphi_y = \varphi_z = 0$ can be singular points on the surface. In fact, if one of the partial derivatives, for example φ_z, is $\neq 0$ at the point Q, then the surface permits a regular parametrization of the form $z = \psi(x, y)$ in a neighborhood of the point Q, from which it follows that Q is a regular point.

Suppose $\varphi_x = \varphi_y = \varphi_z = 0$ at the point $Q(x_0, y_0, x_0)$ on the surface. Expanding the function φ by the Taylor formula in a neighborhood of the point Q, we obtain

$$a_{11}(x - x_0)^2 + a_{22}(y - y_0)^2 + a_{33}(z - z_0)^2 + 2a_{12}(x - x_0)(y - y_0) +$$
$$2a_{13}(x - x_0)(z - z_0) + 2a_{23}(y - y_0)(z - z_0) + R = 0.$$

It turns out that if the quadratic form $\sum a_{ij}\xi_i\xi_j$ is definite, i.e. vanishes only when all the ξ_i equal zero, then in a sufficiently small neighborhood of the point (x_0, y_0, z_0) none of the points in space, except the point (x_0, y_0, z_0), satisfies the equation $\varphi(x, y, z) = 0$. Therefore, the surface $\varPhi$ cannot be defined by the equation $\varphi=0$ in a neighborhood of the point Q.

REMARK. Frequently a surface defined by the equation $\varphi(x, y, z) = 0$ is understood to be the geometric locus of points in space, satisfying the equation $\varphi = 0$. With such a definition of a surface, the point in the case just considered is called an *isolated* singular point.

If the quadratic form $\sum a_{ij}\xi_i\xi_j$ is alternating, but does not factor into the product of two linear forms, the geometric locus of points in space which are near the point (x_0, y_0, z_0) and satisfy the equation $\varphi(x, y, z) = 0$ has a form approximating that of a second degree conic, whose equation is $\varphi(x, y, z) - R = 0$. If the surface is defined as the geometric locus of points in space which satisfy the equation $\varphi(x, y, z) = 0$, then in this case the point (x_0, y_0, z_0) is called a *conical* point.

If the quadratic form $\sum a_{ij}\xi_i\xi_j$ factors into the product of two linear forms, various cases may arise. The point may be a singular point (for example, the point $(0, 0, 0)$ on the surface $xy - z^3 = 0$) or a regular point (for example, the point $(0, 0, 0)$ on the surface $xy - xz^2 = 0$). In this case, it is necessary to investigate further terms in the expansion of the function φ.

EXERCISES AND PROBLEMS FOR CHAPTER IV

1. Write the equation of the surface generated by half-lines which emanate from the point (a, b, c) and intersect the parabola

$$z = 0, \quad y^2 = 2px.$$

ANSWER: $(bz - cy)^2 = 2p(z - c)(az - cx)$.

2. Find the equation of the cylinder with generators parallel to the straight line $x = y = z$, described around the ellipsoid

$$x^2 + 4y^2 + 9z^2 = 1.$$

ANSWER: $(x + 4y + 9z)^2 - 14(x^2 + 4y^2 + 9z^2) = 0$.

3. Find the geometric locus of the projections of the center of the ellipsoid

$$\frac{x^2}{a^2} + \frac{y^2}{b^2} + \frac{z^2}{c^2} = 1$$

onto its tangent planes.

ANSWER: $(x^2a^2 + y^2b^2 + z^2c^2) = (x^2 + y^2 + z^2)^2$.

4. Write the equation of the surface which is obtained by rotating the curve

$$x = \varphi(u), \quad z = \psi(u), \quad y = 0$$

about the z-axis.

ANSWER: $x = \varphi(u) \cos v$, $y = \varphi(u) \sin v$, $z = \psi(u)$.

5. The straight line g moves in space in such a way that the following conditions are satisfied:

a) the straight line always intersects the z-axis orthogonally;

b) the point of intersection of the straight line g with the z-axis moves uniformly with velocity a;

c) the straight line rotates uniformly about the z-axis with angular velocity ω.

Write the equation of the surface which the straight line g describes as it moves.

ANSWER: $x = v \cos \omega u$, $y = v \sin \omega u$, $z = au$.

Here u is the time, and v is the distance of a point on the surface from the z-axis. The surface is called a simple helicoidal surface or a *helicoid*.

6. Suppose three families of surfaces are prescribed by the equations $\varphi(x, y, z) = u = $ constant, $\psi(x, y, z) = v = $ constant, $\chi(x, y, z) = w = $ constant.

Prove that if the Jacobian

$$\frac{D(\varphi, \psi, \chi)}{D(x, y, z)} \neq 0$$

at the point (x_0, y_0, z_0), then all three families can be defined in a neighborhood of this point by the vector equation $r = r(u, v, w)$. The surfaces of distinct families are obtained by setting $u = $ constant, $v = $ constant, $w = $ constant.

7. A translation surface is a surface generated by the successive displacement of one curve along another curve.

Prove that a translation surface can be defined by the equation

$$r = \varphi(u) + \psi(v),$$

where φ and ψ are vector functions of which the first depends only on u, and the second only on v.

8. Show that the surface which is the geometric locus of the midpoints of segments whose endpoints lie on two given curves, is a translation surface.

9. Find the singular curve on the pseudosphere

$$x = \sin u \cos v, \quad y = \sin u \sin v, \quad z = \cos u + \ln \tan u/2.$$

ANSWER: The singular curve is $u = \pi/2$.

CHAPTER V

FUNDAMENTAL CONCEPTS FOR SURFACES WHICH ARE RELATED TO THE CONCEPT OF CONTACT

§ 1. Tangent plane to a surface. Suppose Φ is a surface and P is a point on Φ; let α be any plane passing through the point P. We take a point Q on the surface Φ and denote its distance from the point P and from the plane α by d respectively h (see Fig. 15).

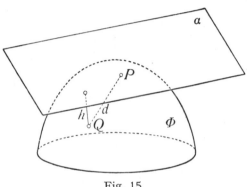

We shall call the plane α the *tangent plane* to the surface Φ at the point P if the ratio $h/d \to 0$ when $Q \to P$.

Fig. 15

THEOREM. *A smooth surface has a unique tangent plane at each of its points.*

If $r = r(u, v)$ *is any smooth parametrization of the surface, then the tangent plane at the point* $P(u, v)$ *is parallel to the vectors* $r_u(u, v)$ *and* $r_v(u, v)$.

PROOF. We shall assume the surface Φ has a tangent plane α at the point $P(u, v)$. Suppose n is a unit vector which is perpendicular to the plane α. The distance d from the point $Q(u+\Delta u, v + \Delta v)$ to the point $P(u, v)$ equals $|r(u + \Delta u, v + \Delta v) - r(u, v)|$. The distance from the point Q to the plane α equals $|((r(u + \Delta u, v + \Delta v) - r(u, v)) \cdot n|$. Hence we have

$$h/d = \frac{|(r(u + \Delta u, v + \Delta v) - r(u, v)) \cdot n|}{|r(u + \Delta v, v + \Delta v) - r(u, v)|}.$$

According to our definition, $h/d \to 0$ when Δu and Δv independently tend to zero. In particular,

$$\frac{|(r(u + \Delta u, v) - r(u, v)) \cdot n|}{|r(u + \Delta u, v) - r(u, v)|} \to 0$$

as $\Delta u \to 0$.

But

$$\frac{|(r(u + \Delta u, v) - r(u, v)) \cdot n|}{|r(u + \Delta u, v) - r(u, v)|} =$$

$$= \frac{\left| \dfrac{r(u + \Delta u, v) - r(u, v)}{\Delta u} \cdot n \right|}{\left| \dfrac{r(u + \Delta u, v) - r(u, v)}{\Delta u} \right|} \to \frac{|r_u(u, v) \cdot n|}{|r_u(u, v)|}.$$

Thus we have

$$r_u(u, v) \cdot n = 0.$$

Since $r_u(u, v) \neq 0$ ($r_u(u, v) \times r_v(u, v) \neq 0$), equality, $r_u(u, v) \cdot n = 0$, is possible only in the case when the vector $r_u(u, v)$ is parallel to the plane α.

One shows in an analogous way that the vector $r_v(u, v)$ is also parallel to the plane α and inasmuch as the vectors $r_u(u, v)$ and $r_v(u, v)$ are different from zero and are not parallel, ($r_u(u, v) \times r_v(u, v) \neq 0$), the tangent plane is unique, provided it exists.

We shall now prove the existence of the tangent plane. Suppose the plane α is parallel to the vectors $r_u(u, v)$ and $r_v(u, v)$. We shall show that it is the tangent plane to the surface at the point $P(u, v)$.

We have

$$h/d = \frac{|(r(u + \Delta u, v + \Delta v) - r(u, v)) \cdot n|}{|r(u + \Delta u, v + \Delta v) - r(u, v)|} =$$

$$= \frac{|(r_u \cdot n)\Delta u + (r_v \cdot n)\Delta v + \varepsilon_1 \sqrt{\Delta u^2 + \Delta v^2}|}{|r_u \Delta u + r_v \Delta v + \varepsilon_2 \sqrt{\Delta u^2 + \Delta v^2}|} =$$

$$= \frac{\left| (r_u \cdot n) \dfrac{\Delta u}{\sqrt{\Delta u^2 + \Delta v^2}} + (r_v \cdot n) \dfrac{\Delta v}{\sqrt{\Delta u^2 + \Delta v^2}} + \varepsilon_1 \right|}{\left| r_u \dfrac{\Delta u}{\sqrt{\Delta u^2 + \Delta v^2}} + r_v \dfrac{\Delta v}{\sqrt{\Delta u^2 + \Delta v^2}} + \varepsilon_2 \right|}$$

where $|\varepsilon_1|$ and $|\varepsilon_2|$ tend to zero when $\Delta u, \Delta v \to 0$.

We shall assume that there exists a sequence of pairs Δu, Δv tending to zero such that the corresponding ratio $h/d > \varepsilon > 0$. The sequence of pairs Δu, Δv contains a subsequence for which the ratios

$$\frac{\Delta u}{\sqrt{\Delta u^2 + \Delta v^2}} \quad \text{and} \quad \frac{\Delta v}{\sqrt{\Delta u^2 + \Delta v^2}}$$

will converge. Suppose ξ and η are the limiting values of these expressions. Obviously, $\xi^2 + \eta^2 = 1$. Passing to the limit of the ratios h/d with respect to the chosen subsequence of the sequence of pairs Δu, Δv we obtain

$$h/d \to \frac{|(r_u \cdot n)\xi + (r_v \cdot n)\eta|}{|r_u \xi + r_v \eta|} \, .$$

Since $r_u \cdot n = 0$, $r_v \cdot n = 0$, and $\xi r_u + \eta r_v \neq 0$ (r_u and r_v are not parallel), $h/d \to 0$. But this contradicts the fact that all the values of h/d near the limit are, by assumption, greater than $\varepsilon > 0$.

This completes the proof of the theorem.

It is not difficult to write down the equation of the tangent plane once we know its direction.

Suppose $\tilde{r}$ is the radius vector of any point on the tangent plane to the surface at the point $P(u, v)$. Then the vectors $\tilde{r} - r(u, v)$, $r_u(u, v)$, $r_v(u, v)$ are parallel to the tangent plane and, consequently, their triple product vanishes. It follows that the equation of the tangent plane is

$$(\tilde{r} - r(u, v), r_u(u, v), r_v(u, v)) = 0.$$

Suppose the surface is defined by the equations

$$x = x(u, v), \quad y = y(u, v), \quad z = z(u, v).$$

It follows from the vector equation of the tangent plane that the equation of the tangent plane corresponding to this representation of the surface will be

$$\begin{vmatrix} \tilde{x} - x(u, v), & \tilde{y} - y(u, v), & \tilde{z} - z(u, v) \\ x_u(u, v) & y_u(u, v) & z_u(u, v) \\ x_v(u, v) & y_v(u, v) & z_v(u, v) \end{vmatrix} = 0.$$

The equation of the tangent plane to the surface, given by the equation $z = z(x, y)$, is obtained from the equation just found. It suffices to note that defining the surface by means of the equation

$z = z(x, y)$ is only an abbreviation for the parametric representation

$$x = u, \quad y = v, \quad z = z(u, v).$$

Therefore, the equation of the tangent plane in the case when the surface is defined by the equation $z = z(x, y)$ will be

$$\begin{vmatrix} \tilde{x} - x, & \tilde{y} - y, & \tilde{z} - z \\ 1 & 0 & z_x(x, y) \\ 0 & 1 & z_y(x, y) \end{vmatrix} = 0,$$

or

$$\tilde{z} - z - p(\tilde{x} - x) - q(\tilde{y} - y) = 0,$$

where p and q denote the first partial derivatives of the function $z(x, y)$ with respect to x and y, respectively.

Finally, we find the equation of the tangent plane for the case when the surface is defined by the equation $\varphi(x, y, z) = 0$. Suppose (x, y, z) is a point on the surface at which $\varphi_x{}^2 + \varphi_y{}^2 + \varphi_z{}^2 \neq 0$ and $x = x(u, v)$, $y = y(u, v)$, $z = z(u, v)$ is any smooth parametrization of the surface in a neighborhood of this point. If we replace x, y, z in the equation of the surface by $x(u, v)$, $y(u, v)$, $z(u, v)$ we obtain an identity with respect to u and v.

Differentiating this identity, we obtain

$$\varphi_x x_u + \varphi_y y_u + \varphi_z z_u = 0,$$
$$\varphi_x x_v + \varphi_y y_v + \varphi_z z_v = 0$$

at the point (x, y, z). If we consider these equations as a system of equations in φ_x, φ_y, φ_z then, solving it, we obtain

$$\frac{\varphi_x}{\begin{vmatrix} y_u & z_u \\ y_v & z_v \end{vmatrix}} = \frac{\varphi_y}{\begin{vmatrix} z_u & x_u \\ z_v & x_v \end{vmatrix}} = \frac{\varphi_z}{\begin{vmatrix} x_u & y_u \\ x_v & y_v \end{vmatrix}}.$$

In the case of the parametric representation of the surface, the equation of the tangent plane is

$$(\tilde{x} - x)\begin{vmatrix} y_u & z_u \\ y_v & z_v \end{vmatrix} + (\tilde{y} - y)\begin{vmatrix} z_u & x_u \\ z_v & x_v \end{vmatrix} + (\tilde{z} - z)\begin{vmatrix} x_u & y_u \\ x_v & y_v \end{vmatrix} = 0.$$

Taking the proportion obtained above into consideration, we obtain the equation of the tangent plane to the surface $\varphi(x, y, z) = 0$ at the point (x, y, z) in the form

$$(\tilde{x} - x)\varphi_x + (\tilde{y} - y)\varphi_y + (\tilde{z} - z)\varphi_z = 0.$$

The *normal* to the surface at the point P is the straight line passing through P perpendicular to the tangent plane at this point.

Writing down the equation of the normal to the surface, once we know the equation of the tangent plane, for the different cases of definition of the surface, does not present any difficulty and hence is left to the reader as an exercise.

§ 2. Lemma on the distance from a point to a surface. Contact of a curve with a surface.

Suppose Φ is a surface and Q is any point in space. The distance of the point Q from the surface Φ is the greatest lower bound of the distances of points on the surface from the point Q. If the point Q lies on the surface then, obviously, its distance from the surface equals zero.

LEMMA. *Suppose Φ is a smooth surface defined by the equation $\varphi(x, y, z) = 0$. Suppose $\varphi_x{}^2 + \varphi_y{}^2 + \varphi_z{}^2 \neq 0$ at the point $O(x_0, y_0, z_0)$ on the surface.*

If $Q(x, y, z)$ is a point in space near O, but not lying on the surface, then substituting the coordinates of the point Q into the equation of the surface we obtain a quantity λ which has the order of the quantity h, which is the distance of the point Q from the surface, in the sense that the ratio λ/h tends to a definite limit, different from zero, when the point Q tends to O, remaining outside the surface.

PROOF. Since the point O belongs to the surface Φ, there exists an $\varepsilon > 0$ such that all the points in space at a distance less than or equal to ε from the point O and satisfying the equation $\varphi(x, y, z) = 0$, belong to the surface Φ.

Suppose the point Q is at a distance less than $\varepsilon/2$ from the point O. Suppose P_n is a sequence of points on the surface whose distances from Q tend to the distance from this point to the surface Φ. The points P_n form a bounded sequence (their distances from Q are less than $\varepsilon/2$), and therefore the sequence P_n contains a convergent subsequence. Without loss of generality, we can assume that the sequence P_n itself converges to some point P. In virtue of the continuity of the function φ in a neighborhood of the point O the point P satisfies the equation $\varphi(x, y, z) = 0$. It follows from this that the point P belongs to the surface Φ. Thus, if a point Q is sufficiently close to O, the greatest lower bound of the distances of points on the surface from the point Q is attained for some point P belonging to the surface.

We shall now show that the segment PQ is directed along the normal to the surface at the point P. Suppose $r = r(u, v)$ is any smooth parametrization of the surface at the point P and that a is the radius vector of the point Q. Since the function $(r(u, v) - a)^2$ attains its minimum at the point P, we must have

$$(r - a) \cdot r_u = 0,$$
$$(r - a) \cdot r_v = 0,$$

but this means that the segment PQ is directed along the normal to the surface at the point P.

Suppose $\bar{x}, \bar{y}, \bar{z}$ are the coordinates of the point P and that ξ, η, ζ are the direction cosines of the normal to the surface at the point P. The coordinates of the point Q are x, y, z and h is the distance between the points P and Q (Fig. 15).

We have

$$\bar{x} = x + \xi h, \quad \bar{y} = y + \eta h, \quad \bar{z} = z + \zeta h.$$

Since the point P belongs to the surface, we have

$$\varphi(x + \xi h, y + \eta h, z + \zeta h) = 0.$$

It follows that

$$\varphi(x, y, z) + h(\varphi_x \xi + \varphi_y \eta + \varphi_z \zeta) + h^2 R = 0,$$

where R is bounded in a neighborhood of the point O.

Dividing this equality by h and passing to the limit as $Q \to O$, we obtain

$$\frac{\varphi(x, y, z)}{h} \to - (\varphi_x \xi + \varphi_y \eta + \varphi_z \zeta)_{(O)}.$$

The expression in the right member is different from zero inasmuch as it is the scalar product of the parallel nonzero vectors (ξ, η, ζ) and $(\varphi_x, \varphi_y, \varphi_z)$.

This completes the proof of the lemma.

We shall now apply the lemma just proved to the problem of contact of a curve with a surface.

Suppose Φ is an elementary surface and let γ be a curve having the point O in common with Φ. Suppose h is the distance of an arbitrary point Q of the curve from the surface Φ and let d be the distance of the point Q from the point O. We shall say that the curve γ has contact of order n with the surface if $h/d^n \to 0$ when $Q \to 0$.

THEOREM. *Suppose Φ is an elementary regular surface and γ is a regular curve having a common point O. Suppose $\varphi(x, y, z) = 0$ is the equation of the surface in a neighborhood of the point O where $\varphi_x{}^2 + \varphi_y{}^2 + \varphi_z{}^2 \neq 0$ at the point O; $x = x(t), y = y(t), z = z(t)$ is a regular parametrization of the curve γ in a neighborhood of the point O.*

Then a necessary and sufficient condition that the curve γ have contact of order n with the surface Φ at the point O is that the conditions

$$\varphi(x(t), y(t), z(t)) = 0, \quad \frac{d}{dt}\varphi = 0, \quad \cdots, \quad \frac{d^n}{dt^n}\varphi = 0$$

be satisfied for the value of t corresponding to the point O.

PROOF. Suppose the value $t = t_0$ corresponds to the point O. As $Q \to 0$, $t \to t_0$.

According to the lemma, $\varphi(x(t), y(t), z(t))$ is of order equal to the distance of the point Q from the surface Φ. It follows that a necessary and sufficient condition that the curve γ have contact of order n with the surface Φ is that

$$\frac{\varphi(x(t), y(t), z(t))}{|r(t) - r(t_0)|^n} = \frac{\dfrac{\varphi(x(t), y(t), z(t))}{|t - t_0|^n}}{\left|\dfrac{r(t) - r(t_0)}{t - t_0}\right|^n} \to 0 \text{ as } t \to t_0.$$

Since

$$\left|\frac{r(t) - r(t_0)}{t - t_0}\right| \to |r'(t_0)| \neq 0,$$

this means that

$$\frac{\varphi(x(t), y(t), z(t))}{(t - t_0)^n} \to 0 \text{ as } t \to t_0.$$

But this is possible if and only if the function $\varphi(x(t), y(t), z(t))$ and its derivatives up to and including the n-th order vanish for $t=t_0$.

This completes the proof of the theorem.

We shall now find the osculating sphere to the curve, i.e. a sphere which has contact of order three with the curve.

Suppose $r = r(s)$ is the natural parametrization of the curve.

The equation of the sphere is $(r - a)^2 = R^2$, where a is the position vector of the center of the sphere and R is its radius. If we substitute $r = r(s)$ into this equation and differentiate three times with respect to s we obtain

$$(r - a) \cdot \tau = 0,$$
$$(r - a) \cdot k_1 n + 1 = 0,$$
$$(r - a) \cdot (k_1' n - k_1^2 \tau - k_1 k_2 b) = 0.$$

It follows that

$$(r - a) \cdot k_1 k_2 b + k_1'/k_1 = 0.$$

Thus,

$$(r - a) \cdot \tau = 0,$$
$$(r - a) \cdot n = - 1/k_1,$$
$$(r - a) \cdot b = - k_1'/k_1^2 k_2.$$

Hence we have

$$R = |r - a| = \sqrt{\left(\frac{1}{k_1}\right)^2 + \left(\frac{k_1'}{k_1^2 k_2}\right)^2},$$

$$a = r + (a - r) = r + n/k_1 + b k_1'/k_1^2 k_2.$$

§ 3. Osculating paraboloid. Classification of points on a surface.

Suppose Φ is a regular (twice continuously differentiable) surface and let P be a point on Φ. Suppose U is a paraboloid containing the point P with axis parallel to the normal to the surface at the point P. Denote the distance from any point Q on the surface to the paraboloid and to the point P respectively, by h and d.

The paraboloid U is called the *osculating paraboloid* of the surface at the point P if the ratio $h/d^2 \to 0$ as $Q \to P$. In this connection, we do not exclude the cases when the paraboloid degenerates into a parabolic cylinder or into a plane.

THEOREM. *At every point P of a regular (twice continuously differentiable) surface Φ there exists a unique osculating paraboloid U, which in particular cases may degenerate into a parabolic cylinder or a plane.*

PROOF. We introduce rectilinear cartesian coordinates x, y, z in space taking the point P for origin of coordinates and the tangent plane at the point P as the x, y-plane, and the normal to the tangent plane, i.e. the normal to the surface, as the z-axis. We shall show that the surface Φ may be defined in a neighborhood of the point P

by means of the equation $z = \varphi(x, y)$ where φ is a twice differentiable function of x and y such that $\varphi_x = \varphi_y = 0$ at the point P. In fact, the surface Φ, as we know, permits at least one representation of the three forms, $z = \varphi(x, y)$, or $y = \psi(x, z)$, or $x = \chi(y, z)$, where φ, ψ and χ are twice continuously differentiable functions. For our choice of coordinate axes, the requirement that the functions ψ and χ be twice differentiable excludes the second and third represen- tations. In fact, if the surface Φ can be defined by means of the equation $y = \psi(x, z)$ or $x = \chi(y, z)$ in a neighborhood of the point P, then the equation of the tangent plane at the point P would have the form $\tilde{y} - \psi_x\tilde{x} - \psi_z\tilde{z} = 0$, or $\tilde{x} - \chi_y\tilde{y} - \chi_z\tilde{z} = 0$. In neither one of these cases do we obtain the plane $\tilde{z} = 0$, which is the tangent plane by assumption. Thus, the surface Φ permits a representation by means of the equation $z = \varphi(x, y)$ in a neighborhood of the point P, and since the tangent plane to the surface Φ at the point P, $\tilde{z} - \varphi_x\tilde{x} - \varphi_y\tilde{y} = 0$, must be the x, y-plane, φ_x and φ_y vanish at the point P. This completes the proof of the assertion.

The equation of the paraboloid U, containing the point P and having its axis parallel to the z-axis, and also its degenerate forms, the parabolic cylinder and plane, have the form

$$z - (a_1x + b_1y + a_{11}x^2 + a_{12}xy + a_{22}y^2) = 0.$$

We shall assume that the osculating paraboloid U exists at the point P. We shall show that it is unique. Suppose

$$z - (a_1x + b_1y + a_{11}x^2 + a_{12}xy + a_{22}y^2) = 0$$

is the equation of the osculating paraboloid. According to the lemma of the preceding section, substituting the coordinates of the point Q on the surface into the equation of the paraboloid we obtain a quantity λ which has the same order as the distance of the point Q from the paraboloid in the sense that the ratio λ/h tends to a limit when $Q \to P$. It follows from this that $\lambda/d^2 \to 0$ as $Q \to P$.

We expand the function $\varphi(x, y)$ according to Taylor's formula in a neighborhood of the origin of the coordinate system. We obtain

$$\varphi(x, y) = \tfrac{1}{2}(rx^2 + 2sxy + ty^2) + (x^2 + y^2)\varepsilon_1(x, y),$$

where r, s, t denote the derivatives of the function φ and $\varepsilon_1(x, y) \to 0$ when $x, y \to 0$. Substituting the coordinates $x, y, \varphi(x, y)$ of the point

Q on the surface into the equation of the paraboloid, we obtain

$$\lambda = -a_1 x - a_2 y + \tfrac{1}{2}\{(r - 2a_{11})x^2 + 2(s - a_{12})xy + (t - 2a_{22})y^2\} + \\ + (x^2 + y^2)\varepsilon_1(x, y).$$

The square of the distance of the point Q from P is

$$d^2 = x^2 + y^2 + \varphi^2(x, y) = x^2 + y^2 + (x^2 + y^2)\varepsilon_2(x, y),$$

where $\varepsilon_2(x, y) \to 0$ as $Q \to P$.

Since the ratio λ/d^2 tends to zero when x and y independently tend to zero, this will hold if and only if, say, $y = 0$ and $x \to 0$. But in this case,

$$\lambda/d^2 = \frac{-a_1 x + \tfrac{1}{2}(r - 2a_{11})x^2 + x^2\varepsilon_1}{x^2 + x^2\varepsilon_2}$$

and, consequently, $\lambda/d^2 \to 0$ as $x \to 0$ only when $a_1 = 0$ and $2a_{11} = r$. It can be shown, in an analogous manner, that $a_2 = 0$ and $2a_{22} = t$. Finally, we show that $a_{12} = s$. To this end, we assume that x and y tend to zero, but in such a way that x always equals y. Then

$$\lambda/d^2 = \frac{(s - a_{12})x^2 + x^2\varepsilon_1}{2x^2 + 2x^2\varepsilon_2}.$$

It is clear from this that the condition $\lambda/d^2 \to 0$ as $x \to 0$ implies the equality $a_{12} = s$.

Thus, if the osculating paraboloid at the point P exists, it is unique. Its equation with respect to the coordinate system we have chosen is

(*) $$z - \tfrac{1}{2}(rx^2 + 2sxy + ty^2) = 0.$$

We shall now show that the paraboloid (*) is indeed the osculating paraboloid.

In fact, for this paraboloid we have

$$\lambda/d^2 = \frac{(x^2 + y^2)\varepsilon_1}{x^2 + y^2 + (x^2 + y^2)\varepsilon_2} \to 0 \text{ as } x, y \to 0.$$

This completes the proof of the theorem.

We shall now find the osculating paraboloid at the point $P(u, v)$ in the case of an arbitrary parametric representation of the surface $r = r(u, v)$.

We introduce, in space, the cartesian coordinates x, y, z, taking the point P as the origin of coordinates, and the directions of the vectors r_u, r_v, n as the directions of the coordinate axes. The vectors r_u, r_v, n themselves are taken as basis vectors.

Consider the paraboloid

$$z = \tfrac{1}{2}\{(r_{uu} \cdot n)x^2 + 2(r_{uv} \cdot n)xy + (r_{vv} \cdot n)y^2\}.$$

We shall show that it is the osculating paraboloid at the point P.

Suppose $Q(u + \Delta u, v + \Delta v)$ is a point on the surface near P.

We draw a straigth line through Q parallel to the normal at the point P. This line cuts the paraboloid at the point Q' with coordinates $x = \Delta u(1 + \varepsilon_1)$, $y = \Delta v(1 + \varepsilon_2)$, z, where ε_1 and $\varepsilon_2 \to 0$ as Δu, $\Delta v \to 0$.

The distance from the point Q to Q' is

$$h' = |(r(u + \Delta u, v + \Delta v) - r(u, v)) \cdot n -$$
$$- \tfrac{1}{2}\{(r_{uu} \cdot n)x^2 + 2(r_{uv} \cdot n)xy + (r_{vv} \cdot n)y^2\}|.$$

Expanding $r(u + \Delta u, v + \Delta v)$ according to the Taylor formula and replacing x and y by $\Delta u(1 + \varepsilon_1)$ and $\Delta v(1 + \varepsilon_2)$, we obtain

$$h' = (\Delta u^2 + \Delta v^2)\varepsilon,$$

where $\varepsilon \to 0$ when Δu, $\Delta v \to 0$.

The distance between the points Q and P equals

$$|r(u + \Delta u, v + \Delta v) - r(u, v)| = |r_u \Delta u + r_v \Delta v + \varepsilon \sqrt{\Delta u^2 + \Delta v^2}|.$$

In order to show that the indicated paraboloid is the osculating paraboloid, it suffices to show that the ratio $h'/d^2 \to 0$ as $Q \to P$, since the distance from the point Q to the paraboloid is less than or equal to h'. But

$$h'/d^2 = \frac{(\Delta u^2 + \Delta v^2)\varepsilon}{(r_u \Delta u + r_v \Delta v + \varepsilon' \sqrt{\Delta u^2 + \Delta v^2})^2} = \frac{\varepsilon}{\left(\dfrac{r_u \Delta u + r_v \Delta v}{\sqrt{\Delta u^2 + \Delta v^2}} + \varepsilon'\right)^2}.$$

And since

$$\left| \frac{r_u \Delta u + r_v \Delta v}{\sqrt{\Delta u^2 + \Delta v^2}} \right|$$

is bounded below as Δu, $\Delta v \to 0$ and ε and $\varepsilon' \to 0$, $h'/d^2 \to 0$.

This completes the proof of the assertion.

The existence and uniqueness of the osculating paraboloid at every point of a regular surface permits us to make the following classification of points on a surface.

1. A point on a surface is called an *elliptic* point if the osculating paraboloid at this point is an elliptic paraboloid (see Fig 16*a*).

2. A point on a surface is called a *hyperbolic* point if the osculating paraboloid at this point is a hyperbolic paraboloid (Fig. 16*b*).

3. A point on a surface is called a *parabolic* point if the osculating paraboloid at this point degenerates into a parabolic cylinder (Fig. 16*c*).

4. A point on a surface is called an *umbilical* point if the osculating paraboloid at this point degenerates into a plane (i.e. the tangent plane to the surface at this point) (see Fig. 16*d*).

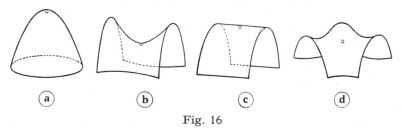

Fig. 16

§ 4. Envelope of a family of surfaces, depending on one or two parameters.

Suppose {S} is a family of smooth surfaces depending on one or two parameters. A surface F is called the *envelope* of the family if the following conditions are satisfied: 1) for every point P on the surface F one can find a surface in the family which is tangent to F at the point P, 2) every surface in the family is tangent to F, 3) no surface in the family has a region in common with F.

EXAMPLE. A smooth surface which does not contain pieces of a plane, is the envelope of its tangent planes. The family of tangent planes may be either a one parameter (cylinder) or a two parameter (e.g. sphere) family.

In geometry and its applications, the problem frequently arises of finding the envelope for a given family. This problem is resolved, to the extent known, by the following theorems.

THEOREM 1. *Suppose* {F_α} *is a family of smooth surfaces, depending on the parameter* α, *defined by the equations*

$$\varphi(x, y, z, \alpha) = 0.$$

Then, if the smooth surface F is the envelope of this family, it satisfies the equations

$$\varphi(x, y, z, \alpha) = 0, \quad \varphi_\alpha(x, y, z, \alpha) = 0$$

in the sense that for every point (x, y, z) on the surface F one can give a value of α such that both the equations $\varphi = 0$ and $\varphi_\alpha = 0$ are satisfied by the four quantities x, y, z, and α.

THEOREM 2. *The envelope of a two parameter family of smooth surfaces*

$$\varphi(x, y, z, \alpha, \beta) = 0$$

satisfies the equations

$$\varphi(x, y, z, \alpha, \beta) = 0, \quad \varphi_\alpha(x, y, z, \alpha, \beta) = 0,$$
$$\varphi_\beta(x, y, z, \alpha, \beta) = 0.$$

In order to simplify the discussion, we shall make some auxiliary assumptions concerning the nature of enveloping of the surfaces of the family by the surface F. Namely, we shall assume, that for every point P of the envelope we can specify a region G_P of variation of the parameters of the family, satisfying the following conditions:

1. For each point Q of the surface F, near P, only one surface of the family can be found having parameters belonging to G_P.

2. If u, v is any smooth parametrization of the surface F and $\alpha(u, v)$, $\beta(u, v)$ (which reduces to only $\alpha(u, v)$ in the case of a one parameter family) are parameters of the surface, tangent to F at the point (u, v), then $\alpha(u, v)$ and $\beta(u, v)$ are smooth functions of u and v.

Under such auxiliary assumptions concerning the nature of enveloping F by surfaces of the family, the proof of both theorems is rather easy. We begin with the first theorem.

The surface of the family which is tangent to the surface F at the point (u, v) has parameter $\alpha(u, v)$. Hence, we have the identity

$$\varphi(x(u, v), y(u, v), z(u, v), \alpha(u, v)) \equiv 0.$$

Differentiating this identity with respect to u and v, we get

$$\varphi_x x_u + \varphi_y y_u + \varphi_z z_u + \varphi_\alpha \alpha_u = 0,$$
$$\varphi_x x_v + \varphi_y y_v + \varphi_z z_v + \varphi_\alpha \alpha_v = 0.$$

But, in virtue of the fact that the surfaces F and F_α are tangent, we have

$$\varphi_x x_u + \varphi_y y_u + \varphi_z z_u = 0,$$
$$\varphi_x x_v + \varphi_y y_v + \varphi_z z_v = 0.$$

Therefore,

$$\varphi_\alpha \alpha_u = 0, \quad \varphi_\alpha \alpha_v = 0.$$

Let us assume that $\varphi_\alpha \neq 0$ at the point P. Then $\varphi_\alpha \neq 0$ in some neighborhood of the point P also and, consequently, $\alpha_u = \alpha_v = 0$ in this neighborhood, i.e. $\alpha = $ constant. But this means that the envelope F has a region in common with the surface F_α of the family, which is impossible. So, $\varphi_\alpha = 0$ at the point P. This proves Theorem 1.

We shall prove Theorem 2. As in the case of a one parameter family, we have the identity

$$\varphi(x(u, v), y(u, v), z(u, v), \alpha(u, v), \beta(u, v)) \equiv 0.$$

Differentiating this identity and using the condition that the surfaces of the family are tangent to the envelope, we obtain

$$\varphi_\alpha \alpha_u + \varphi_\beta \beta_u = 0,$$
$$\text{(*)} \qquad \varphi_\alpha \alpha_v + \varphi_\beta \beta_v = 0.$$

We shall assume that at least one of the two quantities φ_α and φ_β does not vanish at the point P. Then it is also different from zero in some neighborhood of the point P. It follows from equalities (*) that

$$\begin{vmatrix} \alpha_u & \alpha_v \\ \beta_u & \beta_v \end{vmatrix} = 0$$

in this neighborhood, and this means that the functions α and β which are parameters of the family are dependent. But this is impossible, inasmuch as the family must essentially depend on two parameters. So, $\varphi_\alpha = \varphi_\beta = 0$ at the point P. This completes the proof of Theorem 2.

§ 5. Envelope of a family of planes, depending on one parameter. Suppose F is the envelope of a one parameter family of planes. We shall explain the structure of the surface F.

Suppose

$$r \cdot b(\alpha) + a(\alpha) = 0$$

is the equation of the planes of the family in the vector form.

Without loss of generality, we can assume that the vector b is a unit vector, inasmuch as the equation can always be divided by $|b(\alpha)|$ $(b(\alpha) \neq 0)$. Further, we must exclude the case when b does not depend on α, since a family of parallel planes does not have an envelope. In fact, b is the normal vector to the envelope, and therefore $b \cdot dr = 0$. If b is a constant vector, it follows from this that $b \cdot r = $ constant, i.e. the envelope is a plane. A plane of the family, tangent to the envelope, has, in this case, a region in common with it, which is impossible.

In the sequel, the independence of b and α will be excluded by a somewhat greater requirement. Namely, we shall assume that $b'(\alpha) \neq 0$.

The envelope F satisfies the equations

(*) $$r \cdot b + a = 0, \quad r \cdot b' + a' = 0.$$

We shall denote the set of all points in space satisfying the system (*) by M, and we shall first explain the structure of the set M. Obviously, if the point (x_0, y_0, z_0) belongs to the set M, then the entire straight line g_{α_0}, defined by the equations

$$r \cdot b(\alpha_0) + a(\alpha_0) = 0, \quad r \cdot b'(\alpha_0) + a'(\alpha_0) = 0,$$

where α_0 is the value of the parameter which together with x_0, y_0, z_0 satisfies system (*), also belongs to M. Thus, the set M consists of a one parameter set of straight lines in space.

We consider three planes

(**) $$r \cdot b + a = 0, \quad r \cdot b' + a' = 0, \quad r \cdot b'' + a'' = 0,$$

of which the first two define the envelope. The following three fundamental assumptions can be made regarding these three planes:

1. The three planes (**) have no common points for any value of α.

2. The three planes (**) intersect in a unique point S which is the same for all values of α.

3. The three planes (**) intersect in the point $S(\alpha)$ whose position depends essentially on α in this sense that if $\tilde{r}(\alpha)$ is the position vector of the point $S(\alpha)$, then $\tilde{r}'(\alpha) \neq 0$.

We shall consider the first case. Since the planes (**) do not intersect, they are parallel to some straight line. Suppose $n(\alpha)$ is a unit vector along this line. We then have

$$b \cdot n = 0, \quad b' \cdot n = 0, \quad b'' \cdot n = 0.$$

Differentiating the first two equalities, we obtain

$$b' \cdot n + b \cdot n' = 0, \quad b'' \cdot n + b' \cdot n' = 0.$$

It follows that $b \cdot n' = 0$, $b' \cdot n' = 0$. Since, furthermore, $n' \cdot n = 0$, we have $n' = 0$. So, n does not depend on α. Further, the vector $b \times b'$ is nonzero, and its direction is constant, since it is parallel to the vector n ($b \cdot n = 0$, $b' \cdot n = 0$). The position vector of any point in M can be represented in the form

$$r = \lambda b + \mu b' + \nu (b \times b').$$

λ and μ are easily found from equation (*). And we then obtain the equation of the position vector of M in the form

$$r = (-a)b + (-a'/b'^2)b' + \nu (b \times b'),$$

where α and ν are the parameters. It is easy to verify that $r_\alpha \times r_\nu \neq 0$. Thus, in the first case, M is a cylindrical surface. The envelope F has a region on this surface.

In the second case, we obtain a conic surface. Its equation is the same as for a cylindrical surface, but the direction of the vector $b \times b'$ depends on α. If we take the point S for the origin of coordinates, then, as follows from equation (*), $a = 0$, $a' = 0$, and the equation of the surface assumes the simple form

$$r = \nu (b \times b').$$

As in the first case, it is easy to verify that $r_\alpha \times r_\nu \neq 0$ everywhere except at the point $S(\nu = 0)$.

We now consider the third case. The position vector of any point in M can be written in the form

(***) $$r = \tilde{r} + \nu (b \times b').$$

For fixed α, the vector function r gives the straight line of intersection of the planes (*). We shall show that the vectors $\tilde{r}'$ and $b \times b'$ are parallel.

In fact, we have

$$\tilde{r} \cdot b + a \equiv 0, \quad \tilde{r} \cdot b' + a' \equiv 0, \quad \tilde{r} \cdot b'' + a'' \equiv 0.$$

Differentiating the first identity and subtracting the second equation from it, we obtain $\tilde{r}' \cdot b = 0$. Analogously, from the second and third equations we obtain $\tilde{r}' \cdot b' = 0$, whence we have $\tilde{r}' \| b \times b'$.

Now it is not difficult to show that the vector function (***) defines some surface in the region $v \neq 0$. In fact,

$$r_\alpha \times r_v = (\tilde{r}' + v(b \times b')') \times (b \times b') = v(b \times b'') \times (b \times b') \neq 0.$$

Thus, in the neighborhood of every point not belonging to the curve $r = \tilde{r}(\alpha)$, the set M represents a surface. We shall show that this surface is generated by the tangents to the curve $r = \tilde{r}(\alpha)$. In fact, for fixed α equation (***) is the equation of the tangent to the curve $r = \tilde{r}(\alpha)$, since the vectors r' and $b \times b'$ are parallel. Thus, the surface M is generated by the tangents to the curve $r = \tilde{r}$.

The results of the present section may be summarized by the following theorem.

THEOREM. *The envelope of a one parameter family of planes is, in most cases, a region either on a cylindrical surface or on a conic surface, or on a surface generated by the tangents to a space curve.*

It is easy to check directly that conversely, in each of these cases the tangent planes form a one parameter family. It is suggested that the reader verify this fact as an exercise.

EXERCISES FOR CHAPTER V

1. Write the equation of the tangent plane to the ellipsoid

$$\frac{x^2}{a^2} + \frac{y^2}{b^2} + \frac{z^2}{c^2} = 1$$

at the point (x', y', z').

ANSWER: $\dfrac{xx'}{a^2} + \dfrac{yy'}{b^2} + \dfrac{zz'}{c^2} = 1.$

2. Write the equation of the tangent plane to the sphere

$$x = a \cos v \sin u, \quad y = a \cos v \cos u, \quad z = a \sin v$$

at the point $(0, 0, a)$.

ANSWER: $z - a = 0.$

3. Show that all the tangent planes to the surface defined by the equation

$$z = x\varphi(y/x)$$

pass through the origin of coordinates.

4. Show that the surfaces

$$x^2 + y^2 + z^2 = \alpha x,$$
$$x^2 + y^2 + z^2 = \beta y,$$
$$x^2 + y^2 + z^2 = \gamma z,$$

intersect orthogonally.

5. Show that the normals to the surface

$$x = \varphi(u) \cos v, \quad y = \varphi(u) \sin v, \quad z = \psi(u)$$

intersect the z-axis.

6. Find the surface formed by the normals to the surface

$$y = x \tan z$$

along the straight line

$$y = x, \quad z = \pi/4.$$

ANSWER: Hyperbolic paraboloid.

7. Write the equation of the osculating paraboloid to the ellipsoid defined in Exercise 1 at the point $(0, 0, c)$.

ANSWER: $z = c\left(1 - \tfrac{1}{2}\left(\dfrac{x^2}{a^2} + \dfrac{y^2}{b^2}\right)\right).$

8. Investigate the character of the points (elliptic, hyperbolic, parabolic, umbilic) on second degree surfaces.

9. Find the position of the center and the radius of the osculating sphere of the helix

$$x = a \cos t, \quad y = a \sin t, \quad z = bt$$

at the point $(a, 0, 0)$.

ANSWER: Center $(- b^2/a, 0, 0)$; radius $a + b^2/a$.

10. Find the envelope of the family of spheres

$$(x - a)^2 + y^2 + z^2 = 1 \ (- \infty < a < \infty).$$

ANSWER: Cylinder $y^2 + z^2 = 1$.

11. Find the envelope of the family of planes which form a tetrahedron of constant volume with the coordinate planes, x, y, $z > 0$.

ANSWER: $xyz =$ constant.

PROBLEMS AND THEOREMS FOR CHAPTER V

1. Prove that if a smooth surface Φ and a plane α have only one point P in common, then the plane α is the tangent plane to the surface at the point P.

2. Prove that the tangent planes to a translation surface

$$r = U(u) + V(v)$$

along every translation curve (curves $u = $ constant and $v = $ constant) are parallel to some straight line.

3. Prove that the family of confocal ellipsoids, one sheeted and two sheeted hyperboloids, defined, as is known, by the equations

$$\frac{x^2}{a^2 - \lambda} + \frac{y^2}{b^2 - \lambda} + \frac{z^2}{c^2 - \lambda} = 1,$$

intersect orthogonally.

4. Prove that if a surface is tangent to a plane along some curve, then all the points of this curve are either parabolic points or umbilical points.

5. Suppose Φ is a surface and P is a point on Φ; let α be the tangent plane at the point P. Prove the following assertions:

a) if the point P is elliptical, then all points on the surface Φ sufficiently close to P lie on one side of the plane α;

b) if the point P is hyperbolic, then points can be found on the surface arbitrarily close to P which lie on either side of the plane α;

c) if the point P is parabolic or umbilical, then either case may arise (give examples).

6. Prove that under a projective, in particular an affine, transformation, the property of a point being elliptic, hyperbolic, or an umbilical point, remains unchanged.

7. Prove that if all the points on a curve γ on a surface are umbilical points then the curve is a plane curve.

8. We shall say that a curve is *spherical* if all its points belong to some sphere.

Suppose $r = r(t)$ is some curve and $P(t_0)$ is an arbitrary point on it. A necessary and sufficient condition that this curve be spherical is that the curve defined by the equation

$$r = \frac{r(t) - r(t_0)}{|r(t) - r(t_0)|^2}$$

be plane. Prove this assertion.

9. Suppose γ is an arbitrary curve on the surface Φ passing through the point P. Show that the tangent to the curve at P lies in the tangent plane to the surface at this point.

10. Suppose Π is the osculating paraboloid to the surface Φ at the point P. Prove that an arbitrary curve on the surface passing through P has contact of order two with the paraboloid Π at this point.

11. Prove that for an arbitrary analytic transformation of space

$$x' = \varphi_1(x, y, z), \quad y' = \varphi_2(x, y, z), \quad z' = \varphi_3(x, y, z),$$

where φ_1, φ_2, φ_3 are analytic functions with nonzero Jacobian, the property of a curve and surface to have contact of a given order, remains unchanged.

12. Prove that if the boundary of a surface lies in a plane, then either this surface is a region in this plane, or the surface contains elliptic points.

Prove that a closed surface contains elliptic points.

13. Prove that if a straight line has second order contact with a surface then this line lies entirely on the surface.

14. Prove that the family of surfaces defined by the equations

$$\varphi(x, y, z) = \alpha,$$

where φ is a regular function in the variables x, y, z, does not have an envelope.

15. If all the normals to a surface intersect some straight line, then the surface is a surface of revolution. Prove this assertion.

16. Prove that if the normals to a surface pass through a common point, then this surface is either a sphere or a region on a sphere.

CHAPTER VI

FIRST QUADRATIC FORM OF A SURFACE AND CONCEPTS RELATED TO IT

Suppose Φ is a regular surface, $r = r(u, v)$ is any regular parametrization of Φ, and n is the unit normal vector to the surface at the point (u, v).

In the theory of surfaces, an important role is played by three quadratic forms which are related to the surface:

$$dr^2, \quad -dr \cdot dn, \quad dn^2.$$

The first quadratic form $I = dr^2$ is positive definite inasmuch as it assumes only nonnegative values and vanishes only when $du = dv = 0$. In fact, if $dr^2 = 0$, then $dr = r_u du + r_v dv = 0$. And since $r_u \times r_v \neq 0$, this is possible only when $du = dv = 0$.

We shall use the notation $r_u^2 = E$, $r_u \cdot r_v = F$, $r_v^2 = G$ for the coefficients of the first quadratic form of the surface. Thus,

$$I = dr^2 = (r_u du + r_v dv)^2 = r_u^2 du + 2r_u \cdot r_v du dv + r_v^2 dv^2 =$$
$$= E \, du^2 + 2F \, du dv + G \, dv^2.$$

In the present chapter we shall consider a number of concepts for surfaces which are related to the first quadratic form.

§ 1. Length of a curve on a surface. Suppose Φ is a simple surface and γ is a curve. We shall say that the curve γ lies on the surface Φ if every point of the curve γ belongs to the surface.

Let P_0 be a point which the curve and the surface have in common, suppose $r = r(u, v)$ is any parametrization of the surface in a neighborhood of the point P_0, and let $r = r(t)$ be any parametrization of the curve in a neighborhood of this point. Suppose u_0, v_0 and t_0 are the values of the parameters corresponding to the point P_0.

For sufficiently small δ each point $P(t)$ of the curve, $|t - t_0| < \delta$, belongs to a parametrized neighborhood of the point P_0 on the surface. Consequently, each point $P(t)$ is uniquely assigned the values $u(t)$ and $v(t)$ in such a way that $r(t) = r(u(t), v(t))$. We shall call the equations $u = u(t)$, $v = v(t)$ the equations of the curve on the surface.

Suppose Φ is a regular surface and γ is a regular curve on Φ. Let $r = r(u, v)$ and $r = r(t)$ be their regular parametrizations in a neighborhood of the point P which satisfy the usual conditions $r_u \times r_v \neq 0$, $r'^2(t) \neq 0$. Then, in the equations of the curve on the surface

$$u = u(t), \quad v = v(t)$$

the functions $u(t)$ and $v(t)$ are regular functions such that $u'^2(t) + v'^2(t) \neq 0$.

To prove this assertion it is sufficient to apply the implicit function theorem to the system of equations

$$x(t) = x(u, v), \quad y(t) = y(u, v), \quad z(t) = z(u, v),$$

which the functions $u(t)$, $v(t)$ satisfy as is known from the above discussion.

Now suppose Φ is a general surface and let γ be a general curve. According to the definition, the surface Φ is the image of some simple surface $\bar{\Phi}$ under a one-to-one continuous mapping φ into space. We shall say that the curve γ lies on the surface Φ if there exists a curve $\bar{\gamma}$ on the surface $\bar{\Phi}$ the image of which is the curve γ under the mapping φ.

It follows from this that if $r = r(u, v)$ is a parametrization of the surface in a neighborhood of the point $\varphi(P)$ and $r = r(t)$ is a parametrization of the curve in a neighborhood of this point, then functions $u = u(t)$, $v - v(t)$ can be found satisfying the equality $r(t) = r(u(t), v(t))$. Thus, a curve on a surface can always be given in the neighborhood of each point by means of the equations $u=u(t)$, $v = v(t)$, where, if the surface and curve are regular, then $u(t)$ and $v(t)$ are regular functions.

We now consider the length of a curve on a surface. Suppose Φ is a regular surface and $r = r(u, v)$ is its regular parametrization. Let γ be a regular curve on the surface which is given by the equations $u = u(t)$, $v = v(t)$. We shall find an expression for the arc length of a segment of the curve with endpoints at the points $P_0(t_0)$ and $P(t)$. We have

$$s(t_0, t) = \int_{t_0}^{t} |r'(t)|\,dt = \int_{t_0}^{t} |r'(u(t), v(t))|\,dt =$$

$$= \int_{\gamma(P_0, P)} |dr(u, v)| \quad = \int_{\gamma(P_0, P)} \sqrt{I},$$

where I is the first quadratic form of the surface.

We see that in order to measure the lengths of curves on a surface it is sufficient to know the first quadratic form of the surface. In this connection, we say that the first quadratic form defines a *metric* on the surface and it is frequently called a *linear surface element*.

The first quadratic form does not define the surface uniquely. It is easy to introduce examples of various surfaces which have the same quadratic forms for corresponding parametrizations. But, generally speaking, for two surfaces taken arbitrarily, there does not exist a parametrization for which the first quadratic forms of the surfaces coincide. We shall come back to this question later.

§ 2. Angle between curves on a surface. We shall now introduce the notion of *direction* on a surface. The direction $(du:dv)$ on a surface Φ given by the equation $r = r(u, v)$ is the direction of the vector $dr = r_u du + r_v dv$. We shall sometimes call this direction simply (d).

The angle between the directions $(du:dv)$ and $(\delta u:\delta v)$ is the angle between the vectors

$$dr = r_u du + r_v dv \text{ and } \delta r = r_u \delta u + r_v \delta v.$$

We shall find an expression for the angle between the directions (d) and (δ). We have

$$dr \cdot \delta r = |dr|\,|\delta r| \cos \vartheta,$$

$$dr^2 = E du^2 + 2F du dv + G dv^2 = I(d),$$

$$\delta r^2 = E \delta u^2 + 2F \delta u \delta v + G \delta v^2 = I(\delta),$$

$$dr \cdot \delta r = E du \delta u + F(du \delta v + dv \delta u) + G du \delta v = I(d, \delta).$$

It follows from this that the expression for $\cos \vartheta$ is

$$\cos \vartheta = I(d, \delta)/\sqrt{I(d) I(\delta)}.$$

We shall say that the curve γ on the surface defined by the equation $r = r(u, v)$ has the direction $(du:dv)$ at the point (u, v) if the vector $dr = r_u du + r_v dv$ is the tangent vector to the curve at this point.

A curve on the surface defined by the equations $u = u(t)$, $v = v(t)$ has the direction $(u'(t):v'(t))$ at the point $(u(t), v(t))$.

If two curves γ and $\bar\gamma$ on the surface Φ have a common point (u, v) then the *angle* between them at the point (u, v) is the angle between their directions at this point. Thus, the angle between curves on a

surface is the angle between tangents to the curves and, consequently, it depends on neither the parametrization of the surface
nor on the parametrization of the curve.

EXAMPLE. The coordinate curves on a surface (i.e. the curves
$u = $ constant and $v = $ constant) have the directions $(0:dv)$, $(\delta u:0)$.
Therefore we have the expression

$$\cos \vartheta = Fdv\delta u/\sqrt{G}dv^2 \sqrt{E}\delta u^2 = F/\sqrt{EG}$$

for the cosine of the angle between the coordinate curves. It follows
from this that the coordinate net on a surface is orthogonal (i.e. the
coordinate curves intersect at right angles) if and only if $F = 0$.

Suppose that in a neighborhood of the point (u_0, v_0) on a regular
surface there is given a family of curves on the surface by means of
the equations $\varphi(u, v) = $ constant, where $\varphi_u^2 + \varphi_v^2 \neq 0$ at the point
(u_0, v_0). We construct a second family of curves which is orthogonal
to the first. To this end, assuming that the second family exists,
we construct the differential equation for the curves of the second
family.

At the point (u, v) the direction of the curves of the first family
will be $(\varphi_v : - \varphi_u)$. If we denote the direction of the curves of the
second family at this point by $(du:dv)$ then the orthogonality condition for these directions will be

$$E\varphi_v du + F(\varphi_v dv - \varphi_u du) - G\varphi_u dv = 0$$

or

(*) $$\qquad (E\varphi_v - F\varphi_u)du + (F\varphi_v - G\varphi_u)dv = 0.$$

This is also the differential equation of the curves of the second
family.

We note that at least one of the coefficients of this equation, that
is, either $(E\varphi_v - F\varphi_u)$ or $(F\varphi_v - G\varphi_u)$ is different from zero, so that
$(E\varphi_v - F\varphi_u)\varphi_v - (F\varphi_v - G\varphi_u)\varphi_u = E\varphi_v^2 - 2F\varphi_v\varphi_u + G\varphi_u^2 \neq 0$.

As is known from the theory of differential equations, there
exists a function $\mu(u, v)$ which is different from zero at the point
(u_0, v_0) (that is, the integrating factor) such that if we multiply
equation (*) by $\mu(u, v)$ the left member becomes the differential of
some function $\psi(u, v)$:

$$\mu\{(E\varphi_v - F\varphi_u)du + (F\varphi_v - G\varphi_u)dv\} = d\psi.$$

The family of curves on the surface is defined by the equation $\psi(u, v) = $
constant, and is the family orthogonal to the given family. In fact, a

curve of the first family has the direction $(\varphi_v : - \varphi_u)$ at the point (u, v), a curve of the second family has the direction $(\psi_v : - \psi_u)$. But

$$\psi_u = \mu(E\varphi_v - F\varphi_u), \quad \psi_v = \mu(F\varphi_v - G\varphi_u).$$

It follows that

$$\mu\{(E\varphi_v - F\varphi_u)\psi_v - (F\varphi_v - G\varphi_u)\psi_u\} = 0.$$

But this is the condition that the directions

$$(\varphi_v : - \varphi_u), \quad (\psi_v : - \psi_u)$$

be orthogonal.

In a neighborhood of the point (u_0, v_0) the surface Φ can be parametrized in such a way that the curves $\varphi =$ constant and $\psi =$ constant are the coordinate curves. In fact, that this be so it is sufficient that the condition

$$\begin{vmatrix} \varphi_u & \varphi_v \\ \psi_u & \psi_v \end{vmatrix} \neq 0$$

be satisfied (see § 3, Chapter IV). But this condition is satisfied inasmuch as

$$- \varphi_u\psi_v + \varphi_v\psi_u = E\varphi_v{}^2 - 2F\varphi_v\varphi_u + G\varphi_u{}^2 \neq 0.$$

Thus, there exists a regular orthogonal parametrization in a neighborhood of every point on the surface which is such that one family of coordinate curves on the surface can be chosen arbitrarily.

§ 3. Surface area.

Suppose F is a smooth surface and that G is a region on F which is bounded by a finite number of piecewise smooth curves (see Fig. 17). We decompose the region G into small regions by means of piecewise smooth curves. Suppose g is one of these regions. We choose an arbitrary point P in the region g and project this region onto the tangent plane at the point P. If the region g is sufficient-

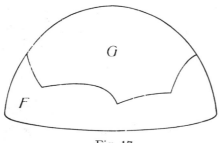

Fig. 17

ly small, then this projection is one-to-one and we obtain a region $\bar{g}$ in the tangent plane which is also bounded by piecewise smooth curves. We denote the area of the region $\bar{g}$ by $\sigma(\bar{g})$.

We shall understand the area of the region G on the surface F to be the

$$\lim \Sigma\, \sigma(\tilde{g}),$$

where the summation extends over all regions g in the decomposition of G, and the passage to the limit is effected under the condition that the regions g in the decomposition of G decrease indefinitely with respect to their dimensions.

The above definition of surface area corresponds completely with the graphic representation of the measurement of area, which is usually connected with the decomposition of a surface and the "rectification" of individual pieces. We shall show that the surface area in the sense of the definition given above in reality possesses the characteristic property of additivity, and we shall also find the formula for the computation of area in the case of an arbitrary parametrization of the surface.

We shall assume, for simplicity of derivation, that a unique smooth parametrization $r = r(u, v)$ can be introduced on the surface. The region G on the surface is assigned some region $\tilde{G}$ in the u, v-plane, which is bounded by piecewise smooth curves and to the decomposition of the region $\tilde{G}$ into regions $\tilde{g}$ by means of piecewise smooth curves there corresponds a decomposition of the region G into regions g by means of piecewise smooth curves.

We shall now define the area $\sigma(\tilde{g})$ of the region $\tilde{g}$. To this end, we introduce rectangular cartesian coordinates x, y, z and take the point P on the surface for the origin of coordinates; the tangent plane to the surface at P is taken as the x, y-plane, and the normal to the surface at P is the z-axis.

A piece g of the surface F is given in cartesian coordinates by means of the equations

$$x = x(u, v), \quad y = y(u, v), \quad z = z(u, v), \quad (u, v) \subset \tilde{g}.$$

The equations

$$x = x(u, v), \quad y = y(u, v), \quad (u, v) \subset \tilde{g}$$

define a one-to-one mapping of the region $\tilde{g}$ onto $\bar{g}$. The numbers u, v can be considered to be the curvilinear coordinates in the region $\bar{g}$.

The area of a region, in curvilinear coordinates, is computed, as is known, by the formula

$$\sigma(\tilde{g}) = \iint\limits_{\tilde{g}} \left\|\begin{matrix} x_u & x_v \\ y_u & y_v \end{matrix}\right\| dudv.$$

The vector $r_u \times r_v$ is directed along the normal to the surface and since the normal at the point P coincides with the z-axis, the absolute value of the vector $r_u \times r_v$ at this point is equal to the absolute value of its component on the z-axis, i.e.

$$|r_u \times r_v| = \left\|\begin{matrix} x_u & x_v \\ y_u & y_v \end{matrix}\right\| = |x_u y_v - y_u x_v|.$$

It follows by continuity that for arbitrary u, v in $\tilde{g}$

$$\left\|\begin{matrix} x_u & x_v \\ y_u & y_v \end{matrix}\right\| = |r_u \times r_v| + \varepsilon_g(u, v),$$

where ε_g is arbitrarily small provided the dimensions of the region g are small.

For the sum of the areas $\sigma(\tilde{g})$ we have

$$\Sigma \, \sigma(\tilde{g}) = \Sigma \iint\limits_{\tilde{g}} (|r_u \times r_v| + \varepsilon_g(u, v)) dudv =$$

$$= \iint\limits_{G} |r_u \times r_v| dudv + \Sigma \iint\limits_{\tilde{g}} \varepsilon_g \, dudv.$$

If the decomposition of the region G into regions g is sufficiently fine the quantities ε_g are less than an arbitrary small $\varepsilon > 0$ in virtue of the uniform continuity of $r_u \times r_v$ in $\tilde{G}$. Therefore

$$|\Sigma \iint\limits_{\tilde{g}} \varepsilon_g dudv| < \varepsilon \Sigma \, \sigma(\tilde{g}) = \varepsilon\sigma(\tilde{G}),$$

where $\sigma(\tilde{G})$ is the area of the region $\tilde{G}$.

It follows from this that

$$\Sigma \, \sigma(\tilde{g}) \rightarrow \iint\limits_{\tilde{G}} |r_u \times r_v| dudv$$

when the region g in the decomposition of the region G decreases indefinitely. This also proves the existence of the area and gives us an expression for it:

$$\sigma(G) = \iint |r_u \times r_v| \, dudv.$$

The additivity of surface area follows from the additivity of the integral. In fact, suppose the region G is decomposed by means of piecewise smooth curves into two regions G_1 and G_2, and let $\tilde{G}_1$ and $\tilde{G}_2$ be the corresponding regions in the u, v-plane. We have

$$\iint_{\tilde{G}} |r_u \times r_v| du dv = \iint_{\tilde{G}_1} |r_u \times r_v| du dv + \iint_{\tilde{G}_2} |r_u \times r_v| \, du dv.$$

This means that

$$\sigma(G) = \sigma(G_1) + \sigma(G_2),$$

which expresses the fact that the surface area is additive.

Now, when the additivity of surface area has been proved, in an actual computation of surface area we can decompose a surface into parts and in each of these parts we can make use of its respective parametrization.

In conclusion, we shall show that surface area is defined by only its first quadratic form. In fact,

$$|r_u \times r_v|^2 = r_u^2 r_v^2 - (r_u \cdot r_v)^2 = EG - F^2.$$

It follows that

$$\sigma = \iint \sqrt{EG - F^2} \, du dv.$$

In particular, if the surface is defined by the equation $z = z(x, y)$, we have

$$\sigma = \iint \sqrt{1 + p^2 + q^2} \, dx dy.$$

§ 4. Conformal mapping. Suppose Φ_1 and Φ_2 are regular surfaces. A one-to-one and continuous mapping of the surface Φ_1 onto the surface Φ_2 is said to be *conformal* if it leaves the angles between curves invariant in the sense that corresponding curves on these surfaces intersect at the same angles.

Suppose Φ_1 and Φ_2 are regular surfaces and P_1 and P_2 are points on these surfaces. Let $r = r_1(u, v)$ and $r = r_2(u, v)$ be regular parametrizations of the surfaces Φ_1 and Φ_2 in neighborhoods of the points P_1 and P_2 respectively; the points P_1 and P_2 of these surfaces correspond to the values u_0, v_0 of the parameters u, v. Suppose the coefficients of the first quadratic form of the surface, corresponding to the indicated parametrization, are proportional, i.e.

$$E_1/E_2 = F_1/F_2 = G_1/G_2.$$

Then a mapping of a neighborhood of the point P_1 on the surface Φ_1 onto a neighborhood of the point P_2 on the surface Φ_2 in which points with the same coordinates u, v are set into correspondence, is conformal. To prove this assertion it is sufficient to note that if γ_1 is a curve on the surface Φ_1, defined by the equations $u = u(t)$, $v = v(t)$, then the curve γ_2 on the surface Φ_2 which corresponds to γ_1 is defined by the same equations $u=u(t)$, $v=v(t)$, and then use the formula for the angle between two curves.

THEOREM. *Suppose Φ_1 and Φ_2 are regular surfaces and that P_1, P_2 are arbitrary points on these surfaces.*

Then there exists a conformal mapping of some neighborhood of the point P_1 on the surface Φ_1 onto some neighborhood of the point P_2 on the the surface Φ_2.

The proof of this theorem is based on the possibility of parametrizing a regular surface in a neighborhood of an arbitrary point in such a way that its first quadratic form assumes the form

$$I = \lambda(u, v)(du^2 + dv^2)$$

with this parametrization.

We shall not carry out the proof of this assertion; we shall only point out that the surfaces Φ_1 and Φ_2 are parametrized in neighborhoods of the points P_1 and P_2 respectively in such a way that a conformal mapping of a neighborhood of the point P_1 on the surface Φ_1 onto a neighborhood of the point P_2 on the surface Φ_2 is obtained by identifying points with the same coordinates.

In conclusion, we introduce an example of the conformal mapping of a sphere onto the plane.

Suppose ω is a sphere with radius R and center at the point $(0, 0, R)$. We consider a mapping of this sphere onto the x, y-plane which consists in the projection of the sphere from the point S onto the x, y-plane. Such a projection of the sphere onto a plane is called a *stereographic* projection (see Fig. 18).

We shall establish the connection between the coordinates $\tilde{x}$, $\tilde{y}$, $\tilde{z}$ of a point on the sphere and the coordinates of its image (x, y) in the plane. We have

$$\tilde{x}/x = \tilde{y}/y = (\tilde{z} - 2R)/(-2R),$$

$$\tilde{x}^2 + \tilde{y}^2 + (\tilde{z} - R)^2 = R^2$$

or

$$\tilde{x}^2 + \tilde{y}^2 + (\tilde{z} - 2R)\tilde{z} = 0.$$

In virtue of the first equation, the last equation can be written as

$$\tilde{x}x + \tilde{y}y - 2R\tilde{z} = 0.$$

Solving this equation together with the first one, we obtain

$$\tilde{x} = 4R^2x/(x^2 + y^2 + 4R^2), \quad \tilde{y} = 4R^2y/(x^2 + y^2 + 4R^2),$$
$$\tilde{z} = 2R(x^2 + y^2)/(x^2 + y^2 + 4R^2).$$

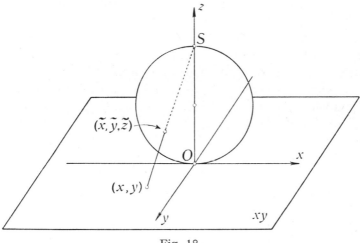

Fig. 18

The first quadratic form of the plane is

$$dx^2 + dy^2$$

and the first quadratic form of the sphere ω is

$$d\tilde{x}^2 + d\tilde{y}^2 + d\tilde{z}^2 = 16R^4(dx^2 + dy^2)/(x^2 + y^2 + 4R^2)^2.$$

From this it is clear that a stereographic projection of the sphere onto a plane is a conformal mapping.

§ 5. Isometric surfaces. Bending of surfaces. The surfaces Φ_1 and Φ_2 are said to be *isometric* if there exists a one-to-one mapping of the surface Φ_1 onto the surface Φ_2 under which corresponding curves on these surfaces have the same length.

Suppose Φ_1 and Φ_2 are regular surfaces and that P_1 and P_2 are points on these surfaces; let $r = r_1(u, v)$, $r = r_2(u, v)$ be regular parametrizations of the surfaces in neighborhoods of the points P_1

and P_2 respectively. Suppose the first quadratic forms of the surfaces, corresponding to these parametrizations, are identical. Then a mapping of a neighborhood of the point P_1 on the surface Φ_1 onto a neighborhood of the point P_2 on the surface Φ_2 in which points with the same coordinates u, v are set into correspondence, is isometric.

In order to prove this assertion, it suffices to note that if the curve γ_1 on the surface Φ_1 is defined by the equations $u = u(t)$, $v = v(t)$, then the curve on the surface Φ_2 which corresponds to it is defined by the same equations $u = u(t)$, $v = v(t)$, and then use the formula for arc length of a curve.

Identical surfaces are, obviously, isometric. The converse is not true in general. It is not difficult to point out examples of isometric surfaces which are not identical. We shall give an example.

The rectangular region $0 < x < \pi/2$, $0 < y < 1$ in the x, y-plane is isometric to the region on the cylinder $x^2 + y^2 = 1$, defined by the conditions $0 < z < 1$, $x > 0$, $y > 0$. It suffices to note that the region on the cylinder indicated permits the parametrization $x = \cos u$, $y = \sin u$, $z = v$, $0 < u < \pi/2$, $0 < v < 1$. A linear element on the cylinder, corresponding to such a parametrization, is $du^2 + dv^2$. From this it is clear that the mapping defined by the equations $x = u$, $y = v$, is isometric.

Suppose Φ_1 and Φ_2 are regular isometric surfaces. Suppose P_1 is any point on the surface Φ_1 and let $r = r_1(u, v)$ be an arbitrary regular parametrization of the surface in a neighborhood of this point.

Then there exists a regular parametrization $r = r_2(u, v)$ in a neighborhood of the point P_2 on the surface Φ_2 such that the points of the surface Φ_1 under this isometry have the same coordinates u, v and the first quadratic forms of the surfaces corresponding to these parametrizations are identical.

In fact, a neighborhood of the point P_1 on the surface Φ_1 is the image of some region G in the u, v-plane under a one-to-one bicontinuous mapping, which assigns the point $P_1(u, v)$ on the surface to the point (u, v) in the plane. Suppose $P_2(u, v)$ is a point on the surface Φ_2 corresponding, under this isometry, to the point $P_1(u, v)$, and that $r_2(u, v)$ is the position vector of P_2. The equation $r = r_2(u, v)$ defines a parametrization of the surface Φ_2 in a neighborhood of the point P_2. The regularity of this parametrization cannot as yet be

established; this will be done in Chapter IX. We shall assume that
the parametrization $r = r_2(u, v)$ of the surface Φ_2 is regular. We
shall show that the first quadratic form of the surface Φ_2 with such
a parametrization coincides with the first quadratic form of the
surface Φ_1.

Suppose γ_1 is any curve on the surface Φ_1 and that $u = u(t)$,
$v = v(t)$ are its equations. The curve on the surface Φ_2 which corresponds to it under the isometry is defined by the same equations.
Therefore

$$\int_{t_0}^{t} \sqrt{E_1 u'^2 + 2F_1 u'v' + G_1 v'^2} \, dt = \int_{t_0}^{t} \sqrt{E_2 u'^2 + 2F_2 u'v' + G_2 v'^2} \, dt.$$

Since this equality holds for any t, the integrands are equal. Inasmuch as the curve γ_1 is completely arbitrary, the functions under
the integral signs are equal for arbitrary values u' and v', and this
is possible only when $E_1 = E_2$, $F_1 = F_2$, $G_1 = G_2$. This completes
the proof of the assertion.

The two preceding assertions can be combined into the following
theorem.

THEOREM. *A necessary and sufficient condition that a neighborhood
of the point P_1 on the regular surface Φ_1 be mapped isometrically onto a
neighborhood of the point P_2 on the regular surface Φ_2 is that there
exist regular parametrizations of neighborhoods of these points such
that the first quadratic forms of the surfaces corresponding to these
parametrizations be identical.*

Since angles between curves on the surface and surface area are
defined by the first quadratic form of the surface, and isometric
surfaces have identical first quadratic forms for corresponding
parametrizations, angles between curves and areas remain unchanged under an isometric mapping, i.e. corresponding regions on
isometric surfaces have identical areas.

We have shown by means of an example that different surfaces
may have identical first quadratic forms for corresponding parametrizations. The question arises, to what degree is the surface
defined by the first quadratic form and does there exist a surface
having an arbitrarily given quadratic form as its first quadratic
form?

It turns out that a surface is far from being defined "in the small"
by its first quadratic form. It is known, for example, that the

following theorem holds. For any sufficiently small neighborhood ω of the point P on an analytic surface there exist surfaces which are isometric to ω and not identical with it.

Some surfaces are defined uniquely "in the large" by the first quadratic form. Thus, for example, an arbitrary regular closed convex surface Φ is uniquely defined by the first quadratic form in the sense that any regular surface Φ' which is isometric to Φ is congruent to Φ. We can itemize a rather extensive class of infinite surfaces which are uniquely defined by the first quadratic form. Any elliptic paraboloid is an example of a surface in this class.

A *bending* of a surface is a continuous deformation of it under which lengths of curves on the surface remain invariant. The bending of a surface can be illustrated graphically by bending a sheet of paper.

Since lengths of curves remain invariant under bending of a surface and consequently at any given moment of bending the surface is isometric to the initial surface, the first quadratic form, for corresponding parametrization, remains invariant under bending.

It turns out that the surface is always bendable "in the small." Thus, for example, the following theorem holds: at every point of an analytic surface which is not an umbilical point there exists a neighborhood permitting a continuous bending. Theorems on bending "in the large" under weaker assumptions concerning regularity are also known.

There exist surfaces "in the large" which do not permit continuous bending. For example, all closed convex surfaces are of this sort.

EXERCISES FOR CHAPTER VI

1. Find the first quadratic form for the surface of revolution

$$x = \varphi(u) \cos v, \quad y = \varphi(u) \sin v, \quad z = \psi(u).$$

ANSWER: $I = (\varphi'^2 + \psi'^2)du^2 + \varphi^2 dv^2$.

2. Show that a surface of revolution can be parametrized in such a way that its first quadratic form will have the form

$$I = du^2 + G(u)dv^2.$$

3. Find the arc length of a curve defined by the equation $u = v$ on a surface with
$$I = du^2 + \sinh^2 u \, dv^2$$
as its first quadratic form.

Answer: $s = |\sinh u_2 - \sinh u_1|$.

4. Find the angle at which the coordinate curves $x = x_0$, $y = y_0$ intersect on the surface $z = axy$.

Answer: $\cos \vartheta = a^2 x_0 y_0 / \sqrt{1 + a^2 x_0^2} \, \sqrt{1 + a^2 y_0^2}$.

5. Show that the coordinate net u, v on the helicoid
$$x = au \cos v, \quad y = au \sin v, \quad z = bv$$
is orthogonal.

6. Find the family of curves which intersect the rectilinear generators $x =$ constant of the hyperboloid $z = axy$ orthogonally.

Answer: $(1 + a^2 x^2)y =$ constant.

7. Find curves on a sphere which intersect the meridians of the sphere at a constant angle (such curves are called loxodromes).

8. Find the area of the quadrilateral on the helicoid (Exercise 5) bounded by the curves
$$u = 0, \quad u = b/a, \quad v = 0, \quad v = 1.$$

Answer: $\sigma = \dfrac{b}{2}(\sqrt{2} + \ln(1 + \sqrt{2}))$.

9. Show that the areas of regions on the paraboloids
$$z = \frac{a}{2}(x^2 + y^2),$$
$$z = axy$$
which project onto the same region in the x, y-plane, are equal.

10. Show that if a surface permits a parametrization for which the coefficients of the first quadratic form do not depend on u and v, then this surface is locally isometric to a plane.

Problems and Theorems for Chapter VI

1. Prove that if $U(x, y)$ and $V(x, y)$ are the real and imaginary parts of a function of the complex variable $x + iy$, then the areas of regions on the surfaces
$$z = U(x, y), \quad z = V(x \, y)$$
which project onto the same region in the x, y-plane, are equal.

Pogorelov, Diff. Geometry.

2. Prove that there exists a conformal mapping of a surface of revolution (Exercise 1) onto a plane for which the meridians of the surface (i.e. the curves $v = $ constant) go over into straight lines which pass through the origin of the coordinate system, and parallels (i.e. the curves $u = $ constant) go over into circles with center at the origin of coordinates.

Consider the particular case when

$$\varphi(u) = \cos u, \quad \psi(u) = \sin u \text{ (sphere)}.$$

3. Prove there exists a conformal mapping of a surface of revolution onto a plane for which the meridians and parallels of the surface go over into the straight lines $x = $ constant, $y = $ constant. Consider the particular case when the surface is a sphere.

4. Prove that it is impossible to map a sphere locally onto a plane.

5. If $U(x, y) + iV(x, y)$ is an analytic function of the complex variable $x + iy$, for which

$$\begin{vmatrix} U_x & V_x \\ U_y & V_y \end{vmatrix} \neq 0$$

at the point (x_0, y_0), then a mapping of a plane onto itself which assigns to the point with cartesian coordinates x, y the point with cartesian coordinates $U(x, y)$, $V(x, y)$, is conformal. Prove this assertion.

6. Suppose

$$ds^2 = Edu^2 + 2Fdudv + Gdv^2$$

is a line element of an analytic surface. We consider the differential equation

$$Edu^2 + 2Fdudv + Gdv^2 = 0$$

in a complex region. Suppose $\varphi(u, v) = $ constant is a solution of this equation and that $U(x, y)$ and $V(x, y)$ are the real and imaginary parts of the function $\varphi(x, y)$. Then if

$$\begin{vmatrix} U_u & V_u \\ U_v & V_v \end{vmatrix} \neq 0$$

a mapping of the surface onto a plane, under which there is assigned to the point (u, v) on the surface the point in the plane with cartesian coordinates U and V, is conformal. (The proof of the theorem in § 4, Chapter VI, for the case of analytic surfaces can be based on this assertion.)

7. A mapping of one surface onto another is said to be *equiareal* if regions which correspond under this mapping have the same areas.

Prove that if a mapping of one surface onto another is conformal and equiareal, then it is isometric.

8. Prove that an arbitrary isometric mapping of a plane onto itself is either a translation or a translation together with a reflection.

9. Suppose Φ_1 and Φ_2 are isometric surfaces and that $r=r_1(u, v)$, $r = r_2(u, v)$ are their parametrizations. An isometric mapping consists in corresponding points with the same coordinates.

Suppose $\Phi_{\lambda,\mu}$ is a surface defined by the equation $r = \lambda r_1(u, v) + \mu r_2(u, v)$. Prove that the surfaces $\Phi_{\lambda,\mu}$ and $\Phi_{\mu,\lambda}$ are isometric.

10. Show that there exists an isometric mapping of the helicoid

$$x = u \cos v, \quad y = u \sin v, \quad z = mv$$

onto the catenoid

$$x = \alpha \cos \beta, \quad y = \alpha \sin \beta, \quad z = m \cosh(\alpha/m),$$

under which the meridians on the catenoid correspond to the rectilinear generators of the helicoid.

11. Prove that an arbitrary helicoid surface permits an isometric mapping onto a surface of revolution, under which parallels correspond to helicoid lines (Bura's theorem).

12_1. A net of curves on a surface is called a Chebyshev net if opposite sides of any quadrilateral formed by curves of the net are equal.

A necessary and sufficient condition that the coordinate net on the surface be a Chebyshev net is that $E_v = G_u = 0$. Prove this theorem.

12_2. Prove that if the coordinate net is Chebyshevian then the coordinates u, v can be chosen so that the linear element on the surface assumes the form

$$ds^2 = du^2 + 2 \cos \omega \, dudv + dv^2,$$

where ω is the angle formed by coordinate curves.

12_3. Prove that on the translation surface

$$r = U(u) + V(v)$$

the coordinates curves form a Chebyshev net.

CHAPTER VII

SECOND QUADRATIC FORM OF A SURFACE AND QUESTIONS ABOUT SURFACE THEORY RELATED TO IT

Suppose Φ is a regular surface and $r = r(u, v)$ is any regular parametrization of Φ, and $n(u, v)$ is the unit normal vector to the surface at the point $P(u, v)$. The second quadratic form of the surface Φ is the quadratic form

$$- dr \cdot dn = (- r_u \cdot n_u)du^2 + (- r_u \cdot n_v - r_v \cdot n_u)dudv + (- r_v \cdot n_v)dv^2.$$

We shall use the following notation for the coefficients of this form:

$$- r_u \cdot n_u = L, \quad - r_u \cdot n_v - r_v \cdot n_u = 2M, \quad - r_v \cdot n_v = N.$$

Since $dr \cdot n = 0$ and, consequently,

$$d(dr \cdot n) = d^2r \cdot n + dr \cdot dn = 0,$$

we have

$$\Pi = d^2r \cdot n = (r_{uu} \cdot n)du^2 + 2(r_{uv} \cdot n)dudv + (r_{vv} \cdot n)dv^2.$$

It follows that

$$L = r_{uu} \cdot n, \quad M = r_{uv} \cdot n, \quad N = r_{vv} \cdot n.$$

Since $n = (r_u \times r_v)/|r_u \times r_v|$, and $|r_u \times r_v| = \sqrt{EG - F^2}$, we have

$$L = \frac{(r_{uu} r_u r_v)}{|r_u \times r_v|} = \frac{\begin{vmatrix} x_{uu} & y_{uu} & z_{uu} \\ x_u & y_u & z_u \\ x_v & y_v & z_v \end{vmatrix}}{\sqrt{EG - F^2}},$$

$$M = \frac{(r_{uv} r_u r_v)}{|r_u \times r_v|} = \frac{\begin{vmatrix} x_{uv} & y_{uv} & z_{uv} \\ x_u & y_u & z_u \\ x_v & y_v & z_v \end{vmatrix}}{\sqrt{EG - F^2}},$$

$$N = \frac{(r_{vv} r_u r_v)}{|r_u \times r_v|} = \frac{\begin{vmatrix} x_{vv} & y_{vv} & z_{vv} \\ x_u & y_u & z_u \\ x_v & y_v & z_v \end{vmatrix}}{\sqrt{EG - F^2}}.$$

In particular, if the surface is defined by the equation $z = z(x, y)$ then

$$L = \frac{z_{xx}}{\sqrt{1 + z_x^2 + z_y^2}}, \quad M = \frac{z_{xy}}{\sqrt{1 + z_x^2 + z_y^2}}, \quad N = \frac{z_{yy}}{\sqrt{1 + z_x^2 + z_y^2}}.$$

Since the equation of the osculating paraboloid to the surface for a suitable choice of coordinates is

$$z = \tfrac{1}{2}(Lx^2 + 2Mxy + Ny^2),$$

the classification of points on the surface as elliptic, hyperbolic, and umbilical points is related to the definition of the second quadratic form of the surface.

§ 1. **Curvature of a curve lying on a surface.** Suppose Φ is a regular surface, that $r = r(u, v)$ is any regular parametrization of Φ, and that γ is a regular curve on the surface which passes through the point $P(u, v)$ and having the direction $(du:dv)$ at this point. Suppose $r = r(s)$ is the natural parametrization of the curve γ.

Consider the scalar product $r'' \cdot n$. The vector r'' is directed along the principal normal to the curve and its magnitude equals the curvature of the curve. From this it follows that

$$r'' \cdot n = k \cos \vartheta,$$

where k is the curvature of the curve and ϑ is the angle formed by the principal normal to the curve and the normal to the surface (Fig. 19). But

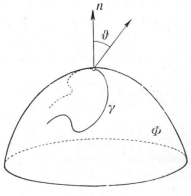

Fig. 19

$$r'' \cdot n = (r_{uu} u'^2 + 2 r_{uv} u' v' + r_{vv} v'^2 + r_u u'' + r_v v'') \cdot n =$$
$$= (r_{uu} \cdot n)u'^2 + 2(r_{uv} \cdot n)u'v' + (r_{vv} \cdot n)v'^2.$$

Therefore

$$k \cos \vartheta = \frac{L du^2 + 2M du dv + N dv^2}{E du^2 + 2F du dv + G dv^2} = \frac{II}{I}.$$

The right member of this equality depends only on the direction

of the curve at the point $P(u, v)$. Thus,

$$k \cos \vartheta = k_0 = \text{constant}$$

at the point $P(u, v)$ for all curves γ which pass through this point and have the same direction at P (i.e. the same tangent).

The equation

$$k \cos \vartheta = k_0 = \text{constant}$$

forms the content of Meusnier's theorem.

The quantity k_0 is called the *normal curvature* of the surface in the given direction $(du:dv)$. To within sign, it is equal to the curvature of the curve, which is obtained by intersecting the surface with a plane perpendicular to the tangent plane and having the direction $(du:dv)$.

REMARK. The set of points common to a surface and the intersecting plane in a neighborhood of the point P does indeed represent a curve. To prove this assertion, it suffices to apply the theorem in § 5, Chapter I.

The normal curvature of the surface Φ at the point $P(u, v)$ in the direction $(du:dv)$ equals the normal curvature of the osculating paraboloid to the surface Φ at the point P in the same direction. In fact, the osculating paraboloid to the surface at the point P permits the following parametrization

$$r = (u - u_0)r_u + (v - v_0)r_v + \frac{n}{2}(L(u - u_0)^2 +$$
$$+ 2M(u - u_0)(v - v_0) + N(v - v_0)^2).$$

From this it is clear that the first and second quadratic forms of the surface and of the osculating paraboloid at the point P coincide, and consequently, the normal curvatures coincide.

We lay off from an arbitrary point $P(u, v)$ of the surface in every direction $(du:dv)$ a segment equal to $|1/k|^{\frac{1}{2}}$ where k is the normal curvature of the surface in this direction. The geometric locus of the endpoints of these segments is called the *indicatrix of curvature* of the surface at the point P (Fig. 20).

We shall now explain what the indicatrix of curvature is. To this end, we introduce cartesian coordinates into the tangent plane to the surface, taking the point of tangency as the origin of coordinates, the straight lines containing the vectors r_u and r_v as the coordinate axes, and the vectors r_u and r_v themselves as the basis vectors.

Suppose x and y are the coordinates of the point of the indicatrix of curvature, corresponding to the direction $(du:dv)$. We have

$$x r_u + y r_v = \left| \frac{1}{k} \right|^{\frac{1}{2}} \frac{r_u du + r_v dv}{|\, r_u du + r_v dv \,|}.$$

Squaring both members of this equation and noting that $x : y = du : dv$, we obtain

$$Ex^2 + 2Fxy + Gy^2 = \frac{Edu^2 + 2Fdudv + Gdv^2}{|Ldu^2 + 2Mdudv + Ndv^2|} =$$

$$= \frac{Ex^2 + 2Fxy + Gy^2}{|Lx^2 + 2Mxy + Ny^2}.$$

It follows that

$$|Lx^2 + 2Mxy + Ny^2| = 1.$$

This is the equation of the indicatrix of curvature.

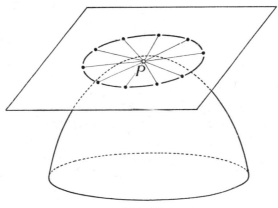

Fig. 20

Thus, the indicatrix of curvature is an ellipse at an elliptic point of the surface $(LN - M^2 > 0)$, a pair of conjugate hyperbolas at a hyperbolic point $(LN - M^2 < 0)$, and a pair of parallel straight line at a parabolic point $(LN - M^2 = 0)$.

§ 2. Asymptotic directions. Asymptotic curves. Conjugate directions. Conjugate nets on a surface. A direction $(du:dv)$ on a regular surface Φ at the point $P(u, v)$ is said to be an *asymptotic*

direction if the normal curvature of the surface in this direction vanishes. Thus, a direction $(du : dv)$ will be asymptotic if and only if the condition

$$Ldu^2 + 2Mdudv + Ndv^2 = 0$$

is satisfied.

From this it follows that asymptotic directions do not exist at an elliptic point, two asymptotic directions exist at a hyperbolic point, one asymptotic direction exists at a parabolic point, and finally, any direction is an asymptotic direction at an umbilical point.

A curve on a surface is said to be an *asymptotic curve* if its direction at each point is asymptotic. From this it follows that

$$Ldu^2 + 2Mdudv + Ndv^2 = 0$$

is the differential equation of the asymptotic curves.

If a straight line lies on a surface then, obviously, it is an asymptotic curve.

We note one simple property of asymptotic curves. The tangent plane to the surface at every point of an asymptotic curve is the osculating plane. In fact, if the curvature of the asymptotic curve γ vanishes at the point P, then the tangent plane to the surface at the point P is already the osculating plane inasmuch as it passes through the tangent to the curve. But if the curvature of the curve γ at the point P is different from zero, then the tangent plane contains the vectors dr and d^2r (the first because the plane is the tangent plane, and the second because the curve γ is an asymptotic curve and, consequently, it satisfies the condition $d^2r \cdot n = 0$). From this it follows that in this case also the tangent plane is the osculating plane to the asymptotic curve.

We shall explain under what conditions the coordinate curves on the surface, $u =$ constant and $v =$ constant, will be asymptotic. Substituting successively $u =$ constant and $v =$ constant into the equation of the asymptotic curves, we conclude that the coordinate net will be asymptotic if and only if the coefficients L and N in the second quadratic form vanish.

In the investigation of surfaces, it is sometimes convenient to parametrize the surface in such a way that the coordinate curves are asymptotic. Such a parametrization is always possible in a neighborhood of a hyperbolic point on the surface (see § 3, Chapter IV).

We now introduce the concept of conjugate directions on a surface.

Suppose P is any point on a regular surface Φ, that $(du : dv)$ and $(\delta u : \delta v)$ are two directions on the surface at the point P, and that g' and g'' are straight lines passing through the point P and having directions $(du : dv)$ and $(\delta u : \delta v)$ respectively. Then the directions $(du : dv)$ and $(\delta u : \delta v)$ are said to be *conjugate directions* if the straight lines g' and g'' are polar conjugate with respect to the osculating paraboloid to the surface at the point P.

It is known from analytic geometry that the condition for polar conjugacy for the paraboloid

$$z = \tfrac{1}{2}(Lx^2 + 2Mxy + Ny^2)$$

is

$$Ldu\delta u + M(du\delta v + dv\delta u)Ndv\delta v = 0.$$

This is also a necessary and sufficient condition that the directions (d) and (δ) be conjugate directions.

It is clear from the conjugacy condition for the directions $(du : dv)$, $(\delta u : \delta v)$ that the diameters of the indicatrices of curvature, having the directions $(du : dv)$, $(\delta u : \delta v)$, are conjugate diameters. This property of conjugate directions could have been taken for their definition.

Suppose we have two families of curves γ_α' and γ_β'' on a surface, forming a net in the sense that through every point of the surface there passes exactly one curve of each family. Then the net of curves, formed by the families γ_α' and γ_β'', is called a *conjugate net* if the curves from different families have conjugate directions at each point.

If the coordinate net is a conjugate net, then the coefficient M of the second quadratic form of the surface vanishes. In order to verify this, it suffices to write the conjugacy condition for the directions $(du : 0)$ and $(0 : \delta v)$.

In a neighborhood of each point P which is not an umbilical point, the surface can be parametrized in such a way that the coordinate net will be conjugate, where one family of curves of this net can be taken arbitrarily just as long as the curves of this family do not have asymptotic directions.

§ 3. Principal directions on a surface. Lines of curvature.

The direction $(du : dv)$ on a surface is called the *principal direction* if the normal curvature of the surface in this direction attains an extremal value. Thus, this is nothing other than the direction which coincides with the directions of the axes of the indicatrix of curvature.

From this it follows that there are two principal directions at each point of the surface in the general case. Since they coincide with the directions of the axes of the indicatrix of curvature, the principal directions are orthogonal and conjugate and, consequently, they satisfy the conditions

$$I(d, \delta) = Edu\delta u + F(du\delta v + dv\delta u) + Gdv\delta v = 0$$

(which is the orthogonality condition),

$$II(d, \delta) = Ldu\delta u + M(du\delta v + dv\delta u) + Ndv\delta v = 0$$

(which is the conjugacy condition).

Eliminating δu and δv from these equations, we obtain

$$\begin{vmatrix} Edu + Fdv & Fdu + Gdv \\ Ldu + Mdv & Mdu + Ndv \end{vmatrix} = 0.$$

This is also a necessary and sufficient condition that the direction $(du : dv)$ be the principal direction. This condition can also be written in another, much more symmetric, form:

$$(*) \qquad \begin{vmatrix} dv^2 & - dudv & du^2 \\ E & F & G \\ L & M & N \end{vmatrix} = 0.$$

The principal directions are not defined in two cases: in the case of an umbilical point, since then any direction is a principal direction at this point (the normal curvature vanishes in any direction), and in the special case of an elliptic point, when the indicatrix of curvature is a circle; such a point is called a *spherical* point. At a spherical point as well as at an umbilical point, any direction is a principal direction. This situation also shows up in the condition (*), which defines the principal directions. It is satisfied identically only in two cases: $L = M = N = 0$ (umbilical point) and in the case the coefficients of the first quadratic form are proportional to the coefficients of the second quadratic form (spherical point).

The normal curvatures to a surface, corresponding to the principal directions, are called the *principal curvatures*.

RODRIGUES'S THEOREM. *If the direction* (d) *is the principal direction then* $dn = - kdr$, *where k is the normal curvature of the surface in this direction. Conversely, if* $dn = \lambda dr$ *in the direction* (d), *then* (d) *is a principal direction.*

PROOF. Suppose (δ) is another principal direction, perpendicular to the first. The vector dn, being perpendicular to n, permits the representation

$$dn = \lambda dr + \mu \delta r.$$

Forming the scalar product of this equation with δr and noting that $dr \cdot \delta r = 0$ in virtue of the conjugacy of the directions (d) and (δ) and $dr \cdot \delta r = 0$ in virtue of the orthogonality of these directions, we obtain

$$\mu \delta r^2 = 0.$$

It follows that $\mu = 0$. Hence, $dn = \lambda dr$. Forming the scalar product of this equation with dr, we get

$$dr \cdot dn = \lambda dr^2.$$

It follows from this that $\lambda = - k$. This completes the first half of the assertion.

We shall now prove the converse assertion. Suppose the direction (d) is such that $dn = \lambda dr$. We shall show that it is a principal direction. Suppose (δ) is the direction perpendicular to (d). Then, forming the scalar product of the equation $dn = \lambda dr$ with δr, we get $dn \cdot \delta r = 0$. But this means that the directions (d) and (δ) are conjugate. Since, moreover, they are orthogonal, they are principal directions.

A curve on a surface is called a *line of curvature* if its direction at every point is the principal direction.

It follows from this that

$$\begin{vmatrix} dv^2 & - dudv & du^2 \\ E & F & G \\ L & M & N \end{vmatrix} = 0$$

is the differential equation of the line of curvature.

If the point P on a surface is not a spherical or umbilical point, then the surface can be parametrized in a neighborhood of P in such a way that the coordinate curves, i.e. the curves $u = $ constant and $v = $ constant will be lines of curvature of the surface. If the surface is parametrized in this way, then the middle coefficients of the first and second quadratic forms will vanish.

In conclusion, we shall prove one theorem which in some cases enables one to find the lines of curvature of a surface quite simply.

THEOREM. *If two surfaces intersect a long some curve γ under a constant angle and if this curve is the line of curvature on one of the surfaces, then it will also be the line of curvature on the other surface.*

PROOF. Differentiating along the curve γ on the first surface, we have

$$dn_1 = \lambda_1 dr.$$

For the second surface, we have

$$dn_2 = \lambda_2 dr + \mu n_1 + \nu n_2.$$

We now form the scalar product of this equation with n_1 and n_2. We then obtain

$$n_1 \cdot dn_2 = \mu n_1{}^2 + \nu n_1 \cdot n_2,$$
$$n_2 \cdot dn_2 = \mu n_1 \cdot n_2 + \nu n_2{}^2.$$

But $n_2 \cdot dn_2 = 0$, $n_1 \cdot dn_2 = d(n_1 \cdot n_2) - n_2 \cdot dn_1 = - n_2 \cdot dn_1 = - n_2 \cdot \lambda dr = 0$. Thus,

$$(**) \qquad \mu n_1{}^2 + \nu n_1 \cdot n_2 = 0, \quad \mu n_1 \cdot n_2 + \nu n_2{}^2 = 0.$$

If a surface is not tangent along the curve γ, then $n_1{}^2 n_2{}^2 - (n_1 \cdot n_2)^2 = |n_1 \times n_2|^2 \neq 0$ and, consequently, equality (**) is possible only if $\mu = \nu = 0$. But then $dn_2 = \lambda_2 dr$ for the second surface, which means that γ is the line of curvature for the second surface.

If a surface is tangent along the curve γ, then we consider a surface which intersects the first surface under a constant nonzero angle. The construction of such a surface in a sufficiently small neighborhood of each point of the curve γ does not present any difficulty. The curve γ will be a line of curvature on this surface. But the surface so constructed intersects the second of the given surfaces at the same angle. It follows from this that the curve γ will be a line of curvature on the second surface.

COROLLARY. *If a sphere (or a plane) intersects any surface at a constant angle, then the intersection curve is a line of curvature.*

This follows from the fact that on a sphere (or on a plane) every curve is a line of curvature.

§ 4. Relation between the principal curvatures of a surface and the normal curvature in an arbitrary direction. Mean and Gaussian curvatures of a surface. We shall express the normal curvature of a surface in an arbitrary direction in terms of the principal normal curvatures. To this end, we introduce rectilinear cartesian coordinates x, y, z taking the tangent plane to the surface at an arbitrary point O as the x, y-plane, and the normal to the surface as the z-axis. We shall choose the directions of the x and y-axes so that they coincide with the principal directions at the point O.

Suppose $z = z(x, y)$ is the equation of the surface in a neighborhood of the point O with such a choice of coordinates. At the point O, $z_x = 0$, $z_y = 0$. Therefore,

$$I = dx^2 + dy^2,$$
$$II = rdx^2 + 2sdxdy + tdy^2$$

at the point O. Since the directions $(0 : dy)$ and $\delta x : 0)$ at the point O are conjugate, being principal directions, we have $s = 0$ and consequently,

$$II = rdx^2 + tdy^2.$$

It follows that the normal curvature in any direction $(dx : dy)$ is

(*)
$$k = \frac{rdx^2 + tdy^2}{dx^2 + dy^2}.$$

Taking the directions $(0 : dy)$ and $(\delta x : 0)$ we see that r and t are the principal curvatures.

Suppose ϑ is the angle formed by an arbitrary direction $(dx : dy)$ with the principal direction $(dx : 0)$, k_ϑ is the normal curvature in this direction, k_1 and k_2 are the principal curvatures corresponding to the directions $(dx : 0)$ and $(0 : \delta y)$, respectively. Then, from the expression for the normal curvature (*), we obtain Euler's formula for the normal curvature in an arbitrary direction,

$$k_\vartheta = k_1 \cos^2 \vartheta + k_2 \sin^2 \vartheta.$$

It follows from the Euler formula that in order to obtain the normal curvature of a surface in any direction, it suffices to know the principal curvatures of the surface. We shall find the expression for the principal curvatures in the case of an arbitrary parametric representation of a surface.

Suppose k_1 and k_2 are the principal curvatures of the surface and suppose for definiteness that $k_1 \geq k_2$. In such a case, as we know, k_1 is a maximum and k_2 is a minimum of the ratio of the quadratic forms,

$$\frac{II}{I} = \frac{L\xi^2 + 2M\xi\eta + N\eta^2}{E\xi^2 + 2F\xi\eta + G\eta^2}.$$

Suppose $\bar{\xi}$, $\bar{\eta}$ are the values of the variables ξ and η for which this ratio attains its maximum (we already know the existence of such ξ and η). Then, for all ξ and η,

$$II - k_1I \leq 0,$$

where equality holds for $\xi = \bar{\xi}$ and $\eta = \bar{\eta}$. If follows from this that for these values

$$(II - k_1I)_\xi' = 0,$$
$$(II - k_1I)_\eta' = 0,$$

i.e.

$$L\bar{\xi} + M\bar{\eta} - k_1(E\bar{\xi} + F\bar{\eta}) = 0,$$
$$M\bar{\xi} + N\bar{\eta} - k_1(F\bar{\xi} + G\bar{\eta}) = 0.$$

Eliminating $\bar{\xi}$ and $\bar{\eta}$ from these equations, we obtain the following equation for k_1

$$\begin{vmatrix} L - k_1E, & M - k_1F \\ M - k_1F, & N - k_1G \end{vmatrix} = 0.$$

Carrying out the analogous reasoning for k_2, we obtain the same equation. Thus, the principal curvatures k_1 and k_2 are the roots of the quadratic equation

$$\begin{vmatrix} L - kE, & M - kF \\ M - kF, & N - kG \end{vmatrix} = 0,$$

i.e.

$$k^2(EG - F^2) - k(LG - 2MF + NE) + LN - M^2 = 0.$$

We shall now define the concepts of mean and Gaussian curvatures of a surface. Half the sum of the principal curvatures of a surface

$$H = \tfrac{1}{2}(k_1 + k_2)$$

is called the *mean curvature* of the surface.

The nomenclature "mean curvature" is justified by the following properties of it.

If k_ϑ and $k_{\vartheta + \frac{\pi}{2}}$ are the normal curvatures of a surface in two mutually perpendicular directions, then half their sum equals the mean curvature of the surface.

The mean value of the normal curvatures of a surface at a given point on the surface

$$\frac{1}{2\pi} \int_0^{2\pi} k_\vartheta \, d\vartheta$$

equals the mean curvature of the surface. Both these properties are obtained without difficulty from Euler's formula.

The product of the principal curvatures of a surface is called the *Gaussian curvature*, or the *total curvature*, of the surface,

$$K = k_1 k_2.$$

We shall find the expression for the mean and Gaussian curvatures of a surface in terms of the coefficients of the first and second quadratic forms.

Inasmuch as the principal curvatures k_1, k_2 of the surface satisfy the equation

$$k^2(EG - F^2) - k(LG - 2MF + NE) + LN - M^2 = 0,$$

then in virtue of the properties of the roots of a quadratic equation we obtain

$$H = \tfrac{1}{2}(k_1 + k_2) = \tfrac{1}{2} \frac{LG - 2MF + NE}{EG - F^2},$$

$$K = k_1 k_2 = \frac{LN - M^2}{EG - F^2}.$$

In particular, if the surface is defined by the equation $z = z(x, y)$, then

$$H = \tfrac{1}{2} \frac{(1 + q^2)r - 2pqs + (1 + p^2)t}{(1 + p^2 + q^2)^{3/2}},$$

$$K = \frac{rt - s^2}{(1 + p^2 + q^2)^2},$$

where p, q, r, s, t is the usual notation for the partial derivatives of the function $z(x, y)$.

We note that the sign of the Gaussian curvature is defined by the expression $LN - M^2$. Therefore, the Gaussian curvature is positive at elliptic points, negative at hyperbolic points, and equal to zero at parabolic and umbilical points.

A necessary and sufficient condition that the point P on a surface be an umbilical point is that the mean and Gaussian curvatures at this point be equal to zero.

In fact, the normal curvature in any direction vanishes at an umbilical point. In particular, the principal curvatures are equal to zero, but then half their sum and their product equals zero, i.e. the mean and Gaussian curvatures vanish. Conversely, if the mean and Gaussian curvatures vanish, then the principal curvatures vanish and, consequently, the normal curvature in any direction equals zero. But then the second quadratic form vanishes identically, i.e. the point P is an umbilical point.

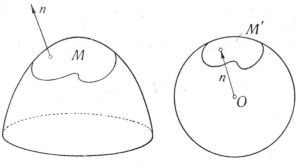

Fig. 21

Suppose M is any set of points on a surface. We mark off from an arbitrary point O unit normal vectors to the surface at points of the set M. The ends of these normals form some set M' on a unit sphere. This set is called the *spherical image* of the set M (Fig. 21).

There exists a remarkable relation among the area of a surface, the area of its spherical image and the Gaussian curvature of the surface. This relation is expressed by the following theorem.

GAUSS'S THEOREM. *The ratio of the area of the spherical image of a region on a surface to the area of this region tends to the absolute value of the Gaussian curvature at a prescribed point O of the surface, when the region shrinks down to this point.*

We shall carry out the proof of this theorem under the assumption that the Gaussian curvature does not vanish at the point O and that the region G, which shrinks to the point O, is bounded by a finite number of piecewise smooth curves. The situation is this that the spherical image of the region G cannot be a region if the Gaussian curvature vanishes at the point O. Therefore, in order to consider the general case, we must define the concept of area for an arbitrary set.

Thus, suppose O is either an elliptic or hyperbolic point on the surface and that G is a region, lying in a sufficiently small neighborhood of the point O, bounded by a finite number of piecewise smooth curves.

We shall parametrize the surface in a neighborhood of the point O in such a way that the coordinate curves which pass through the point O are in the direction of the principal directions at this point.

The equation

$$\tilde{r} = n(u, v),$$

where $n(u, v)$ is a unit normal vector to the surface, represents the parametrization of the unit sphere in a neighborhood of the point O', corresponding to the point O on the surface. In fact, the condition $n_u \times n_v \neq 0$ is satisfied in an obvious manner at the point O' since $n_u = -k_1 r_u$, $n_v = -k_2 r_v$, and by continuity it is also satisfied in some neighborhood of this point. The spherical image G' of the region G, if the region G lies in a sufficiently small neighborhood of the point O, represents a region bounded by a finite number of piecewise smooth curves. Its area is given by

$$\sigma(G') = \iint\limits_G |n_u \times n_v|\, dudv.$$

Since the area of the region G is

$$\sigma(G) = \iint\limits_G |r_u \times r_v|\, dudv,$$

we have

$$\frac{\sigma(G')}{\sigma(G)} \to \frac{|n_u \times n_v|(O)}{|r_u \times r_v|(O)} = |k_1 k_2|.$$

This completes the proof of the theorem.

Pogorelov, Diff. Geometry.

§ 5. Ruled surfaces. A surface Φ is called an *elementary ruled surface* if a straight line passes through every point P of this surface, where the line has an interval, containing P, in common with the surface but the endpoints of this interval do not belong to the surface.

EXAMPLE. Suppose $a(u)$ and $b(u)$ are two vector functions, defined in a neighborhood of the point $u = u_0$, which satisfy the conditions $b(u_0) \neq 0$, $b(u_0) \times a'(u_0) \neq 0$ at this point. Then the vector equation

(*) $r = a(u) + vb(u)$, $|u - u_0| < \varepsilon$, $|v| < \varepsilon$

defines an elementary ruled surface for sufficiently small ε.

In fact, for sufficiently small ε, $r_u \times r_v \neq 0$, inasmuch as $r_u \times r_v = a'(u_0) \times b(u_0) \neq 0$ when $u = u_0$, $v = 0$. If follows from this that for sufficiently small ε equation (*) does indeed define a surface. The fact that this surface is an elementary ruled surface follows from the situation that a straight line $r = a(u') + tb(u')$ passes through any point (u', v') of this surface. The segment $|t| < \varepsilon$ of this line lies on the surface, and its endpoints do not belong to the surface.

A surface Φ is called a *general ruled surface* if each of its points has a neighborhood which is an elementary ruled surface.

Rectilinear segments on a ruled surface are called *rectilinear generators*.

Inasmuch as rectilinear generators pass through every point of a ruled surface, there is a direction at every point of a ruled surface in which the normal curvature of the surface vanishes. It follows from this that a ruled surface cannot have elliptic points. The Gaussian curvature of a ruled surface is negative or equal to zero.

Rectilinear generators are asymptotic curves.

We shall find a local parametric representation of an arbitrary ruled surface, i.e. a parametric representation in a sufficiently small neighborhood of any point P.

We shall distinguish the following cases:
a) The point P is hyperbolic;
b) All points in a sufficiently small neighborhood of the point P are parabolic;
c) All points in a neighborhood of the point P are umbilical points.

In the first case, at least one family of asymptotic curves in a neighborhood of the point P are straight lines. In fact, either all the asymptotic curves in a neighborhood of the point P are straight lines, or one can find asymptotes γ arbitrarily close to P which are not straight lines. But then all asymptotes which intersect γ are straight lines.

If $r = a(u)$ is the equation of the asymptote γ and $b(u)$ is a unit vector in a second asymptotic direction, then the surface can be defined by means of the equation

$$r = a(u) + vb(u)$$

in a neighborhood of the point P.

We shall now consider the second case. In this case, the rectilinear generators are lines of curvature. Only one rectilinear generator passes through each point Q near P. We draw the curve γ, $r = a(u)$, through the point P on a surface in such a way that its direction at the point P does not coincide with the direction of the generator. The unit vector $b(u)$ on the generator is a regular function of u. The surface can be defined by the equation

$$r = a(u) + vb(u)$$

in a neighborhood of the point P.

We finally consider the third case. Since all points near P are umbilical points, and any direction is a principal direction at an umbilical point and the normal curvature in any direction equals zero, by Rodrigues's theorem $dn = 0$ in a neighborhood of the point P. Consequently, $n = n_0 = $ constant. Since $n \cdot dr = 0$, we have $n_0 \cdot (r - r_0) = 0$. Thus, in the third case a sufficiently small neighborhood of the point P is a region on the surface. Suppose a_0 and b_0 are any independent constant vectors, belonging to this plane. Then in a neighborhood of the point P the surface can be defined by means of the equation

$$r = a_0 u + b_0 v.$$

Thus, in all the cases we have considered, a ruled surface permits a parametrization of the form

$$r = a(u) + vb(u)$$

in a sufficiently small neighborhood of every point.

We shall now consider an important class of ruled surfaces, the so-called developable surfaces.

A surface Φ is called a *developable surface* if it is locally isometric to a plane, i.e. if every point of such a surface has a neighborhood which is isometric to a region in a plane.

It turns out that a necessary and sufficient condition that a surface be developable is that its Gaussian curvature vanish everywhere. Thus, developable surfaces may be defined as surfaces with zero Gaussian curvature.

A surface which is the envelope of a one parameter family of planes is a developable surface. In order to verify this, it is sufficient to calculate the Gaussian curvature of the envelope, starting with its parametric representation obtained in § 5, Chapter V.

We shall study the structure of a developable surface in a neighborhood of an arbitrary point P. We shall distinguish two cases:

a) The mean curvature $H = 0$ in a neighborhood of the point P;

b) The mean curvature $H \neq 0$ in a neighborhood of the point P.

In the first case, the principal curvatures of the surface vanish at every point near the point P. Consequently, every point near P is an umbilical point. But then, as was shown above, the point P has a neighborhood which is a plane region.

We shall now consider the second case. We introduce a coordinate net, consisting of lines of curvature, on the surface. Suppose the u-curves (i.e. $v =$ constant) are those lines of curvature along which the normal curvature of the surface vanishes.

By Rodrigues's theorem, $n_u = 0$, since the normal curvature vanishes in the direction of the u-curves. It follows from this that the normals to the surface along the u-curves are parallel.

We shall show that the u-curves are straight lines. We have $r_u \cdot n = 0$. It follows that along a u-curve, $(r - r_0) \cdot n = 0$. Thus, the u-curve lies in a plane. Further, the vector $n_v \neq 0$ is directed along the normal to the u-curve. And since $(n_v)_u = (n_u)_v = 0$, the normals to the u-curves are parallel. But this can hold only when the u-curves are straight lines.

Thus, in both cases, a developable surface is a ruled surface such that the tangent plane remains unchanged along the rectilinear generators. Thus, in the second of the cases considered, the tangent plane depends only on one parameter (v) and, consequently, the surface is the envelope of a one parameter family of planes.

§ **6. Surfaces of revolution.** A surface F is said to be a *surface of revolution* if it is generated by rotating some curve about an axis. Curves of intersection of the surface with planes passing through the axis of ratotion are called *meridians* and curves of intersection with planes perpendicular to the axis are called *parallels* (Fig. 22).

We shall now derive the equation of the surface of revolution which is generated by rotating the curve

$$x = \varphi(u), \quad z = \psi(u)$$

lying in the x, z-plane, about the z-axis. The point $(\varphi(u), 0, \psi(u))$ on the curve γ goes over, upon rotation of the curve through an angle v, into the point

$$(\varphi(u) \cos v, \varphi(u)\sin v, \psi(u)).$$

It follows that the equations of the surface of rotation are

$$x = \varphi(u)\cos v, \quad y = \varphi(u)\sin v, \quad z = \psi(u).$$

The curves $v = $ constant are meridians of the surface and $u = $ constant are parallels.

We shall now find the first quadratic form of the surface. We have

$$E = (\varphi' \cos v)^2 + (\varphi' \sin v)^2 + \psi'^2 = \varphi'^2 + \psi'^2,$$
$$F = (\varphi' \cos v)(-\varphi \sin v) + (\varphi' \sin v)(\varphi \cos v) = 0,$$
$$G = (-\varphi \sin v)^2 + (\varphi \cos v)^2 = \varphi^2.$$

It follows that

$$ds^2 = (\varphi'^2 + \psi'^2)du^2 + \varphi^2 dv^2.$$

We see that the meridians and parallels form an orthogonal net $(F = 0)$. This is, moreover, geometrically obvious.

We now find the second quadratic form. We have

$$L = \frac{\begin{vmatrix} \varphi'' \cos v, & \varphi'' \sin v, & \psi'' \\ \varphi' \cos v & \varphi' \sin v & \psi' \\ -\varphi \sin v & \varphi \cos v & 0 \end{vmatrix}}{EG - F^2} = \frac{\varphi(\psi''\varphi' - \psi'\varphi'')}{\varphi^2(\varphi'^2 + \psi'^2)},$$

$$M = \frac{\begin{vmatrix} -\varphi' \sin v, & \varphi' \cos v, & 0 \\ \varphi' \cos v & \varphi' \sin v & \psi' \\ -\varphi \sin v & \varphi \cos v & 0 \end{vmatrix}}{EG - F^2} = 0,$$

$$N = \frac{\begin{vmatrix} -\varphi \cos v & -\varphi \sin v & 0 \\ \varphi' \cos v & \varphi' \sin v & \psi' \\ -\varphi \sin v & \varphi \cos v & 0 \end{vmatrix}}{EG - F^2} = \frac{\psi'}{\varphi'^2 + \psi'^2}.$$

It follows that

$$II = \frac{\varphi(\psi''\varphi' - \psi'\varphi'')}{\varphi^2(\varphi'^2 + \psi'^2)} \, du^2 + \frac{\psi' dv^2}{\varphi'^2 + \psi'^2}.$$

We see that the parallels and meridians form a conjugate net ($M = 0$). Since, furthermore, this net is orthogonal, parallels and meridians are lines of curvature. This is also clear geometrically, because planes, passing through the axis and perpendicular to the axis intersect the surface of revolution at a constant angle. According to the corollary to the theorem in § 3, Chapter VII, the intersection curves (i.e. the meridians and parallels) must be lines of curvature.

Concerning the first and second quadratic forms of a surface of revolution, it is essential to note that the coefficients of these forms depend only on u.

We shall find the principal curvatures of a surface of revolution. Suppose k_1 is the curvature of a meridian and k_2 is the curvature of a parallel, ϑ is the angle formed by the tangent to the meridian with the axis of the surface. Since the meridian plane intersects the surface orthogonally, the normal curvature of the surface in the direction of the meridian equals the curvature of the meridian, i.e. k_1. According to Meusnier's theorem, we obtain the value $k_2 \cos \vartheta$ for the curvature of the surface in the direction of the parallels. The quantity $k_2 \cos \vartheta$ has a simple geometric interpretation. Namely, if we denote by d the length of the segment of the normal to the surface to the point of intersection with the axis (see Fig. 22), then

$$k_2 \cos \vartheta = 1/d.$$

In concluding this section, we shall construct an example of a surface of revolution with constant negative Gaussian curvature.

Suppose the z-axis is the axis of revolution. The equation of the meridian on the surface in the x, z-plane is $x = x(z)$. The normal curvature of the surface in the direction of the meridian is

$$k_1 = x''/(1 + x'^2)^{3/2}.$$

The normal curvature of the surface in the direction of the parallels is

$$k_2 = -1/\{x(1 + x'^2)^{\frac{1}{2}}\}.$$

It follows that the Gaussian curvature of the surface is

$$K = -x''/\{x(1 + x'^2)^2\}.$$

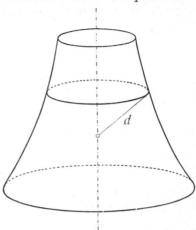

Multiplying this equation by xx', we get

$$Kxx' = \frac{-x'x''}{(1 + x'^2)^2}.$$

Integrating, we have

$$Kx^2 + c = 1/(1 + x'^2)$$

where c is an arbitrary constant.

Fig. 22

Set $c = 1$ so that further integration in terms of elementary functions will be possible. Then

$$Kx^2 = -x'^2/(1 + x'^2).$$

We now set $x' = \tan \vartheta$. Then

$$Kx^2 = -\sin^2 \vartheta, \quad x = \frac{1}{\sqrt{-K}} \sin \vartheta.$$

Further, we have

$$\frac{dz}{dx} = \cot \vartheta, \quad dz = \frac{1}{\sqrt{-K}} \frac{\cos^2 \vartheta}{\sin \vartheta} d\vartheta = \frac{1}{\sqrt{-K}} \left(\frac{1}{\sin \vartheta} - \sin \vartheta \right) d\vartheta.$$

It follows that

$$z = \frac{1}{\sqrt{-K}} (\cos \vartheta + \ln \tan \vartheta/2) + c.$$

The constant c is unessential since it corresponds to a translation of the meridian parallel to the axis.

The equations of the meridian are

$$x = \frac{1}{\sqrt{-K}} \sin \vartheta,$$

$$z = \frac{1}{\sqrt{-K}} (\cos \vartheta + \ln \tan \vartheta/2).$$

This curve is called a *tractrix*. Its distinguishing property is the fact that the segment of the tangent from the point of tangency to the z-axis is constant. Thus, the surface we have just found is obtained by rotating a tractrix. This surface is called a *pseudosphere*. Its equations are

$$x = \frac{1}{\sqrt{-K}} \sin \vartheta \cos \varphi,$$

$$y = \frac{1}{\sqrt{-K}} \sin \vartheta \sin \varphi,$$

$$z = \frac{1}{\sqrt{-K}} (\cos \vartheta + \ln \tan \vartheta/2).$$

Fig. 23 gives us an idea of the shape of the pseudosphere.

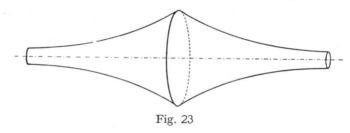

Fig. 23

EXERCISES FOR CHAPTER VII

1. Compute the second quadratic form for the helicoidal surface
$$x = u \cos v, \quad y = u \sin v, \quad z = v.$$
ANSWER: $2dudv/u$.

2. Find the normal curvature of the paraboloid $z = \frac{1}{2}(ax^2 + by^2)$ at the point $(0, 0)$ in the direction $(dx : dy)$.

ANSWER: $k = \dfrac{adx^2 + bdy^2}{dx^2 + dy^2}$.

3. Show that for an arbitrary parametrization of a plane the second quadratic form vanishes identically; show that the second quadratic form is proportional to the first for any parametrization of the sphere.

4. Find the asymptotic lines to the surface

$$z = \frac{x}{y} + \frac{y}{x}.$$

ANSWER: $x = c_1 y,$ $\dfrac{1}{x^2} - \dfrac{1}{y^2} = c_2.$

5. Determine the asymptotic curves to the catenoid

$$x = \cosh u \cos v, \quad y = \cosh u \sin v, \quad z = u.$$

ANSWER: $u + v = $ constant, $u - v = $ constant.

6. Show that on the helicoid one family of asymptotic curves consists of straight lines and that the other consists of helixes.

7. Find the family of curves on the surface

$$ax^2 + by^2 + cz^2 = 1$$

which is conjugate to the family $y = $ constant.

ANSWER: $1 - by^2 = \lambda x^2$, where λ is an arbitrary constant.

8. Show that the translation curves ($u = $ constant, $v = $ constant) on the translation surface

$$r = U(u) + V(v)$$

form a conjugate net.

9. Determine the principal curvatures of the paraboloid

$$z = a(x^2 + y^2)$$

at the point $(0, 0, 0)$.

ANSWER: $2a, 2a$.

10. Determine the lines of curvature on the helicoid

$$x = u \cos v, \quad y = u \sin v, \quad z = cv.$$

ANSWER: $\ln(u + \sqrt{u^2 + c^2}) - v = $ constant,

$\ln(u + \sqrt{u^2 + c^2}) + v = $ constant.

11. Find the lines of curvature of the hyperboloid $z = axy$.

ANSWER: $\dfrac{1}{a}\left(\sqrt{1 + a^2 y^2} + \ln(ay + \sqrt{1 + a^2 y^2})\right) \pm$

$$\pm \dfrac{1}{a}\left(\sqrt{1 + a^2 x^2} + \ln(ax + \sqrt{1 + a^2 x^2})\right) = \text{constant}.$$

12. Find the mean and Gaussian curvatures of the hyperboloid $z = axy$ at the point $x = y = 0$.

ANSWER: $K = -a^2$, $H = 0$.

13. Show that the mean curvature of the helicoid equals zero.

14. Show that the mean curvature of the catenoid

$$z = a \cosh \frac{\sqrt{x^2 + y^2}}{a}$$

equals zero.

15. Show that if the mean curvature of a surface vanishes then its asymptotic net is orthogonal.

PROBLEMS AND THEOREMS FOR CHAPTER VII

1. Suppose $r = r(u, v)$ is an arbitrary surface, (u_k, v_k) is a sequence of points converging to the point (u_0, v_0) and $(a : b)$ is the direction in which the normal curvature to the surface at the point (u_0, v_0) is different from zero.

Show that if

$$\frac{u_k - u_0}{v_k - v_0} \to \frac{a}{b}$$

as $k \to \infty$ then the directions of the lines of intersection of the tangent planes to the surface at the points (u_0, v_0) and (u_k, v_k) converge to the direction conjugate to $(a : b)$.

2. Prove that under a projective, and in particular under an affine, transformation of a surface, a conjugate net goes over into a conjugate net; and an asymptotic net goes over into an asymptotic net.

3. Prove Koenig's theorem: A net on an arbitrary surface is formed by the ̇urves of intersection of the surface with a bundle of planes which pass through an arbitrary straight line g and the contact curves of surface with conicoids having vertices on the straight line g. This net is conjugate.

4. Prove that translation curves on the translation surface

$$r = U(u) + V(v)$$

(i.e. the curves $u = $ constant, $v = $ constant) form a conjugate net.

5. Prove that on the Peterson surfaces

$$r = \frac{\overline{U}(u) + \overline{V}(v)}{U(u) + V(v)},$$

where $\overline{U}$ and $\overline{V}$ are vectors and U and V are scalar functions of the indicated arguments, the families $u = $ constant and $v = $ constant form a conjugate net.

6. If every point on a surface is spherical, then the surface is a sphere or a region on a sphere. Prove this assertion.

7. Find the spherical points on the ellipsoid

$$\frac{x^2}{a^2} + \frac{y^2}{b^2} + \frac{z^2}{c^2} = 1.$$

8. Prove that if the asymptotic lines of different families have nonzero curvatures at their common point, then they have curvatures which are equal in magnitude but opposite in sign.

The absolute value of the curvature equals the absolute value of the Gaussian curvature of the surface at the prescribed point (Beltrand-Enneper theorem).

9_1. Suppose $r(u, v, w)$ is a vector function of the arguments u, v, w. Prove that if

$$r_u \cdot r_v = r_v \cdot r_w = r_w \cdot r_u = 0,$$

then

$$r_{uv} \cdot r_w = r_{vw} \cdot r_u = r_{wu} \cdot r_v = 0.$$

9_2. Suppose we have given three families of surfaces:
$\varphi(x, y, z) = $ constant, $\psi(x, y, z) = $ constant, $\chi(x, y, z) = $ constant, where the Jacobian

$$\frac{D(\varphi, \psi, \chi)}{D(x, y, z)} \neq 0.$$

We say that the indicated families form a *triorthogonal* system of surfaces if any two surfaces from distinct families intersect at right angles.

Prove that the surfaces of different families of a triorthogonal system intersect along the lines of curvature.

9_3. Find the lines of curvature on the second degree surface

$$\alpha x^2 + \alpha y^2 + \gamma z^2 = 1$$

by referring it to a triorthogonal system of confocal second degree surfaces.

10_1. A surface Φ is said to be *parallel* to the surface F if it is the geometric locus of the endpoints of segments of constant length marked off on the normals to the surface F. We shall assume the corresponding points on the surfaces F and Φ to be the endpoints of the segments mentioned in the definition.

Show that

  a) the tangent planes at corresponding points of the surfaces F and Φ are parallel;

  b) the parallel property is dual (i.e. if Φ is parallel to F, then F is parallel to Φ);

  c) the lines of curvature of the surface F correspond to the lines of curvature of the surface Φ.

10_2. If the point P on the surface F is neither a spherical point nor an umbilical point, then in a neighborhood of the point P the surfaces parallel to F and the developable surfaces generated by the normals to the surface F along lines of curvature, form a triorthogonal system of surfaces. Prove this assertion.

10_3. Prove that under an inversion, lines of curvature of a given surface go over into lines of curvature of the transformed surface.

10_4. Prove that under a conformal mapping of space onto itself, a sphere goes over into a sphere or a plane. Basing arguments on this fact, prove in turn that any conformal transformation is obtained by applying a similarity transformation, a translation, a mirror reflexion, and an inversion.

11. Express the mean and Gaussian curvatures of parallel surfaces in terms of the mean and Gaussian curvatures of the given surface and the distance between the parallel surfaces.

12_1. Suppose the surface F is

$$r = f(u, v)$$

undergoes a deformation for which it goes over into the surface F_t in time t

$$r = f(u, v) + t\lambda(u, v)n.$$

Prove that for small t the change in the area of the surface subjected to a deformation equals, to within terms of order t,

$$2T \int_F H d\sigma,$$

where H is the mean curvature of the surface F and $d\sigma$ is an element of area on this surface.

12_2. The surface F is said to be *minimal* if every point P of this surface has a neighborhood bounded by a simple curve γ such that any surface with boundary γ has an area which is greater than or equal to the neighborhood ω of the surface F. Prove that a minimal surface has zero mean curvature.

13. Prove that a spherical mapping of a minimal surface in a neighborhood of every point, which is not an umbilical point, is conformal.

14. Show that the area of a region G bounded by the curve γ on a minimal surface equals

$$s = \tfrac{1}{2} \int\limits_{\gamma} (r, dr, n)$$

(Schwartz's formula).

15. Prove that if a minimal surface is a ruled surface then it is either a plane or a helicoid.

16. Prove that if a minimal surface is a surface of revolution, then it is either a plane or a catenoid.

17. Find by quadratures all surfaces of revolution with constant Gaussian curvature.

CHAPTER VIII

FUNDAMENTAL EQUATIONS OF THE THEORY OF SURFACES

In the two preceding chapters we considered a number of problems concerning the theory of surfaces for the solution of which it was sufficient to know only the first and second quadratic forms of the surface.

The question naturally arises, to what degree do the first and second quadratic forms of the surface define the surface and what conditions ought the quadratic forms

$$Edu^2 + 2Fdudv + Gdv^2,$$
$$Ldu^2 + 2Mdudv + Ndv^2$$

satisfy in order that there exist a surface for which these quadratic forms are the first and second quadratic forms respectively?

The answer to this question will be given in the last section of the present chapter by the Bonnet theorem.

§ 1. The Gauss formula for total curvature of a surface.

We shall now obtain an expression for the Gaussian curvature of a surface in terms of the coefficients of only the first quadratic form and their derivatives.

We already found an expression for the Gaussian curvature in terms of the coefficients of the first and second quadratic forms, namely

$$K = \frac{LN - M^2}{EG - F^2}.$$

Substituting everywhere the expressions for the coefficients of the second quadratic form

$$L = \frac{(r_{uu}r_ur_v)}{\sqrt{EG - F^2}}, \quad M = \frac{(r_{uv}r_ur_v)}{\sqrt{EG - F^2}}, \quad N = \frac{(r_{vv}r_ur_v)}{\sqrt{EG - F^2}}$$

we have

$$K = \frac{1}{(EG - F^2)^2} \{(r_{uu}r_ur_v)(r_{vv}r_ur_v) - (r_{uv}r_ur_v)^2\}.$$

It follows from this, applying the known identity

$$(a_1b_1c_1)(a_2b_2c_2) \equiv \begin{vmatrix} (a_1 \cdot a_2) & (a_1 \cdot b_2) & (a_1 \cdot c_2) \\ (b_1 \cdot a_2) & (b_1 \cdot b_2) & (b_1 \cdot c_2) \\ (c_1 \cdot a_2) & (c_1 \cdot b_2) & (c_1 \cdot c_2) \end{vmatrix},$$

that

$$K = \frac{1}{(EG-F^2)^2} \left\{ \begin{vmatrix} r_{uu} \cdot r_{vv} & r_{uu} \cdot r_u & r_{uu} \cdot r_v \\ r_u \cdot r_{vv} & E & F \\ r_v \cdot r_{vv} & F & G \end{vmatrix} - \begin{vmatrix} r_{uv}^2 & r_{uv} \cdot r_u & r_{uv} \cdot r_v \\ r_u \cdot r_{uv} & E & F \\ r_v \cdot r_{uv} & F & G \end{vmatrix} \right\} =$$

$$= \frac{1}{(EG-F^2)^2} \left\{ \begin{vmatrix} r_{uu} \cdot r_{vv} - r_{uv}^2 & r_{uu} \cdot r_u & r_{uu} \cdot r_v \\ r_u \cdot r_{vv} & E & F \\ r_v \cdot r_{vv} & F & G \end{vmatrix} - \begin{vmatrix} 0 & r_{uv} \cdot r_u & r_{uv} \cdot r_v \\ r_u \cdot r_{uv} & E & F \\ r_v \cdot r_{uv} & F & G \end{vmatrix} \right\}.$$

Differentiating the expressions

$$r_u^2 = E, \quad r_u \cdot r_v = F, \quad r_v^2 = G$$

with respect to u and v, we obtain

$$r_{uu} \cdot r_u = \tfrac{1}{2} E_u,$$
$$r_{uv} \cdot r_u = \tfrac{1}{2} E_v,$$
$$r_{vv} \cdot r_v = \tfrac{1}{2} G_v,$$
$$r_{uv} \cdot r_v = \tfrac{1}{2} G_u,$$
$$r_{uu} \cdot r_v = F_u - \tfrac{1}{2} E_v,$$
$$r_{vv} \cdot r_u = F_v - \tfrac{1}{2} G_u.$$

If we now differentiate the fifth equation with respect to v, the fourth with respect to u, and then subtract the resultant equations termwise, we obtain

$$r_{uu} \cdot r_{vv} - r_{uv}^2 = -\tfrac{1}{2} G_{uu} + F_{uv} - \tfrac{1}{2} E_{vv}.$$

Substituting the values thus obtained into the expression for the Gaussian curvature, we get

$$K = \frac{1}{(EG-F^2)^2} \left\{ \begin{vmatrix} (-\tfrac{1}{2}G_{uu}+F_{uv}-\tfrac{1}{2}E_{vv}), & \tfrac{1}{2}E_u, & (F_u - \tfrac{1}{2}E_v) \\ (F_v - \tfrac{1}{2}G_u) & E & F \\ \tfrac{1}{2}G_v & F & G \end{vmatrix} - \right.$$

$$\left. - \begin{vmatrix} 0, & \tfrac{1}{2}E_v, & \tfrac{1}{2}G_u \\ \tfrac{1}{2}E_v & E & F \\ \tfrac{1}{2}G_u & F & G \end{vmatrix} \right\}.$$

Thus, the Gaussian curvature of a surface may be expressed in terms of the coefficients of the first quadratic form and their derivatives. It follows that the following corollaries hold:

1. Isometric surfaces have the same Gaussian curvature at isometrically corresponding points. In particular, the Gaussian curvature of a surface remains invariant under bending.

2. Since developable surfaces are by definition locally isometric to a plane, and a plane has zero Gaussian curvature, the Gaussian curvature of developable surfaces vanishes everywhere.

3. The first and second quadratic forms of a surface are not independent. Namely, the discriminant $LN - M^2$ of the second quadratic form of a surface may be expressed in terms of the coefficients of the first quadratic form and their derivatives.

In conclusion we note that if a surface is parametrized in such a way that the first quadratic form is

$$I = du^2 + Gdv^2,$$

then the Gaussian curvature of the surface is

$$K = - 1/\sqrt{G}(\sqrt{G})_{uu}.$$

In order to verify this, it suffices to use the Gauss formula.

§ 2. Derived formulas. The derived formulas for a surface are analogous to the Frenet formulas for curves. They yield expressions for the derivatives of the vectors r_u, r_v, n in terms of these vectors and the coefficients of the first and second quadratic forms of the surface. We shall now proceed to obtain these formulas.

Since the vectors r_u, r_v, n do not lie in one plane, an arbitrary vector permits a representation in the form of a linear combination of the vectors r_u, r_v, n. In particular,

$$r_{uu} = \Gamma_{11}{}^1 r_v + \Gamma_{11}{}^2 r_u + \lambda_{11} n,$$
$$r_{uv} = \Gamma_{12}{}^1 r_v + \Gamma_{12}{}^2 r_u + \lambda_{12} n,$$
$$r_{vv} = \Gamma_{22}{}^1 r_u + \Gamma_{22}{}^2 r_v + \lambda_{22} n,$$
$$n_u = \alpha_{11} r_u + \alpha_{12} r_v + \alpha_{10} n,$$
$$n_v = \alpha_{21} r_u + \alpha_{22} r_v + \alpha_{20} n.$$

We shall show that the coefficients $\Gamma_{ij}{}^k$, λ_{ij}, α_{ij} can indeed be expressed in terms of the coefficients of the first and second quadratic forms of the surface.

We note, first of all, that the coefficients α_{10} and α_{20} vanish. To see this, it suffices to form the scalar product of the two equations with n. We then get

$$n_u \cdot n = \alpha_{10}, \quad n_v \cdot n = \alpha_{20}.$$

But

$$n_u \cdot n = \tfrac{1}{2}(n^2)_u = 0, \quad n_v \cdot n = \tfrac{1}{2}(n^2)_v = 0.$$

In order to obtain expressions for α_{11} and α_{12}, we shall form the scalar product of the equation

$$n_u = \alpha_{11} r_u + \alpha_{12} r_v$$

with r_u and r_v. We obtain

$$-L = \alpha_{11} E + \alpha_{12} F,$$
$$-M = \alpha_{11} F + \alpha_{12} G.$$

It follows that

$$\alpha_{11} = \frac{-LG + MF}{EG - F^2}, \quad \alpha_{12} = \frac{LF - ME}{EG - F^2}.$$

In an analogous manner, we obtain

$$\alpha_{21} = \frac{NF - MG}{EG - F^2}, \quad \alpha_{22} = \frac{-NE + MF}{EG - F^2}.$$

In order to obtain the coefficients λ_{11}, λ_{12}, λ_{22} we form the scalar product of the first three formulas with n. We get

$$\lambda_{11} = L, \quad \lambda_{12} = M, \quad \lambda_{22} = N.$$

In order to obtain the expressions for the coefficients $\Gamma_{ij}{}^k$, we form the scalar product of the first three equations with r_u and r_v. We then obtain the following relations for the coefficients $\Gamma_{ij}{}^k$:

$$\begin{cases} \Gamma_{11}{}^1 E + \Gamma_{11}{}^2 F = \tfrac{1}{2} E_u, \\ \Gamma_{11}{}^1 F + \Gamma_{11}{}^2 G = F_u - \tfrac{1}{2} E_v; \end{cases}$$
$$\begin{cases} \Gamma_{12}{}^1 E + \Gamma_{12}{}^2 F = \tfrac{1}{2} E_v, \\ \Gamma_{12}{}^1 F + \Gamma_{12}{}^2 G = \tfrac{1}{2} G_u; \end{cases}$$
$$\begin{cases} \Gamma_{22}{}^1 E + \Gamma_{22}{}^2 F = F_v - \tfrac{1}{2} G_u, \\ \Gamma_{22}{}^1 F + \Gamma_{22}{}^2 G = \tfrac{1}{2} G_v. \end{cases}$$

We can find the expressions for the six coefficients $\Gamma_{ij}{}^k$ from these six equations. We shall not write out the values of the coefficients $\Gamma_{ij}{}^k$; we shall note only that they can be, in distinction to the other coefficients, expressed in terms of only the coefficients of the first quadratic form and their derivatives.

We have thus shown that the derivatives of the vectors r_u, r_v, n can indeed be expressed in terms of the vectors r_u, r_v and n with coefficients depending only on the coefficients of the first and second quadratic forms of the surface.

In conclusion, we shall find the coefficients $\Gamma_{ij}{}^k$ for the case when the first quadratic form of the surface is

$$I = du^2 + G dv^2.$$

If we set $E = 1$, $F = 0$ in the equations for $\Gamma_{ij}{}^k$, we obtain

$$\Gamma_{11}{}^1 = 0, \qquad \Gamma_{11}{}^2 = 0,$$
$$\Gamma_{12}{}^1 = 0, \qquad \Gamma_{12}{}^2 = \tfrac{1}{2} G_u/G,$$
$$\Gamma_{22}{}^1 = -\tfrac{1}{2} G_u, \quad \Gamma_{22}{}^2 = \tfrac{1}{2} G_v/G.$$

§ 3. The Peterson-Codazzi formulas.

We already know that the first and second quadratic forms of a surface are not independent. One of the dependence relations between the coefficients of the first and second quadratic forms of a surface is given by the Gauss formula. It enables one to express the discriminant $LN - M^2$ of the second quadratic form in terms of the coefficients of the first quadratic form and their derivatives.

We now obtain two new relations between the coefficients of the first and second quadratic forms of a surface.

We have the obvious equalities

$$(r_{uu})_v - (r_{uv})_u = 0,$$
$$(r_{vv})_u - (r_{uv})_v = 0,$$
$$(n_u)_v - (n_v)_u = 0.$$

If in these equations, the expressions in parentheses are replaced by the derived expressions given in § 2, and after differentiating, again using the expressions in § 2, we obtain three vector equations of the form

$$A_1 r_u + B_1 r_v + C_1 n = 0,$$
$$A_2 r_u + B_2 r_v + C_2 n = 0,$$
$$A_3 r_u + B_3 r_v + C_3 n = 0,$$

where A_1, A_2, $\cdots$, C_3 are expressions, constructed in a known manner, in the coefficients of the first and second quadratic forms of the surface and their derivatives. We have nine scalar equations from these three vector relations,

$$A_1 = 0, \quad B_1 = 0, \quad C_1 = 0,$$
$$A_2 = 0, \quad B_2 = 0, \quad C_2 = 0,$$
$$A_3 = 0, \quad B_3 = 0, \quad C_3 = 0.$$

It turns out that of these nine relations only three are distinct, of which one is equivalent to the Gauss formula which we obtained earlier and the other two are

$$(EG - 2FF + GE)(L_v - M_u) \\ -(EN - 2FM + GL)(E_v - F_u) \; + \; \begin{vmatrix} E & E_u & L \\ F & F_u & M \\ G & G_u & N \end{vmatrix} = 0,$$

$$(EG - 2FF + GE)(M_v - N_u) \\ -(EN - 2FM + GL)(F_v - G_u) \; + \; \begin{vmatrix} E & E_v & L \\ F & F_v & M \\ G & G_v & N \end{vmatrix} = 0.$$

The last two relations were first obtained by Peterson, in a somewhat different form; they were later obtained by Mainardi and Codazzi.

§ 4. **The existence and uniqueness of a surface with prescribed first and second quadratic forms.** The following theorem, due to Bonnet, holds.

THEOREM. *Suppose*

$$E du^2 + 2F du dv + G dv^2,$$
$$L du^2 + 2M du dv + N dv^2$$

are to arbitrary quadratic forms the first of which is positive definite. Suppose the coefficients of these forms satisfy the Gauss-Peterson-Codazzi conditions. Then there exists a surface, unique to within position in space, for which these forms are the first and second quadratic forms respectively.

PROOF. Let us consider the following system of differential equations for the vector functions ξ, η, ζ:

$$\xi_u = \Gamma_{11}{}^1 \xi + \Gamma_{11}{}^2 \eta + L\zeta,$$
$$\xi_v = \Gamma_{12}{}^1 \xi + \Gamma_{12}{}^2 \eta + M\zeta,$$
$$\eta_u = \Gamma_{12}{}^1 \xi + \Gamma_{12}{}^2 \eta + M\zeta,$$
$$\eta_v = \Gamma_{22}{}^1 \xi + \Gamma_{22}{}^2 \eta + N\zeta,$$
$$\zeta_u = \alpha_{11} \xi + \alpha_{12} \eta$$
$$\zeta_v = \alpha_{21} \xi + \alpha_{22} \eta$$

where the coefficients $\Gamma_{ij}{}^k$ and α_{ij} are expressed, in a known manner, in terms of the coefficients of the prescribed quadratic forms.

It is known from the theory of differential equations that this system has a unique solution for given initial conditions (i.e. the values of ξ, η, ζ are given in some point (u_0, v_0)) if the integrability conditions are satisfied, i.e. if the equations

$$(\Gamma_{11}{}^1\xi + \Gamma_{11}{}^2\eta + L\zeta)_v - (\Gamma_{12}{}^1\xi + \Gamma_{12}{}^2\eta + M\zeta)_u = 0,$$

$$(\Gamma_{12}{}^1\xi + \Gamma_{12}{}^2\eta + M\zeta)_v - (\Gamma_{22}{}^1\xi + \Gamma_{22}{}^2\eta + N\zeta)_u = 0,$$

$$(\alpha_{11}\xi + \alpha_{12}\eta)_v - (\alpha_{21}\xi + \alpha_{22}\eta)_u = 0$$

are identically satisfied in virtue of the equations of the system. Thus, the integrability conditions reduce to the Gauss-Peterson-Codazzi conditions.

Since the Gauss-Peterson-Codazzi conditions are satisfied for the given quadratic forms, the integrability conditions are satisfied for the system of differential equations considered.

Suppose ξ_0, η_0, ζ_0 are three vectors which satisfy the conditions

$$\xi_0{}^2 = E(u_0, v_0), \quad \xi_0 \cdot \eta_0 = F(u_0, v_0), \quad \eta_0{}^2 = G(u_0, v_0),$$

$$\xi_0 \cdot \zeta_0 = 0, \quad \eta_0 \cdot \zeta_0 = 0, \quad \zeta_0{}^2 = 1.$$

Suppose ξ, η, ζ is a solution of our system which satisfies the initial conditions: $\xi(u_0, v_0) = \xi_0$, $\eta(u_0, v_0) = \eta_0$, $\zeta(u_0, v_0) = \zeta_0$.

Since $\xi_v = \eta_u$, there exists a vector function $r(u, v)$ for which $r_u = \xi, r_v = \eta$. We shall show that the surface defined by the vector equation $r = r(u, v)$ has, in a neighborhood of the point (u_0, v_0),

$$Edu^2 + 2Fdudv + Gdv^2$$

as its first quadratic form and

$$Ldu^2 + 2Mdudv + Ndv^2$$

as its second quadratic form.

We shall express the derivatives, with respect to u, v, of the six quantities ξ^2, η^2, ζ^2, $\xi \cdot \eta$, $\eta \cdot \zeta$, $\zeta \cdot \xi$ again in terms of these same quantities, making use of the equations of our system. Then we obtain twelve equations

$$(\xi^2)_u = R_1(\xi^2, \eta^2, \cdots),$$

(*) $$(\xi^2)_v = R_2(\xi^2, \eta^2, \cdots),$$

. . . .

. . . .

$$(\zeta \cdot \xi)_v = R_{12}(\xi^2, \eta^2, \cdots),$$

where $R_1, R_2, \cdots, R_{12}$ are linear homogeneous expressions in $\xi^2, \eta^2,$ $\cdots, \zeta \cdot \xi$.

The twelve equations (*) can be considered as a system of differential equations for $\xi^2, \eta^2, \cdots, \zeta \cdot \xi$. This system, obviously, is satisfied if we replace $\xi^2, \eta^2, \cdots, \zeta \cdot \xi$ by $E, G, \cdots, 0$, respectively. Both these solutions have the same initial conditions (i.e. the same values at the point (u_0, v_0)). From this it follows, in virtue of the uniqueness of the solution, that

$$\xi^2 = E, \quad \eta^2 = G, \quad \xi \cdot \eta = F, \quad \xi \cdot \zeta = 0, \quad \zeta \cdot \eta = 0, \quad \zeta^2 = 1.$$

Since $r_u = \xi, r_v = \eta$, we have

$$r_u{}^2 = \xi^2 = E, \quad r_u \cdot r_v = \xi \cdot \eta = F, \quad r_v{}^2 = \eta^2 = G.$$

Thus, the surface we have constructed has

$$E\,du^2 + 2F\,dudv + G\,dv^2$$

as its first quadratic form.

Further, since $\xi \cdot \zeta = \eta \cdot \zeta = 0$ and $\zeta^2 = 1$, ζ is a unit normal vector to the constructed surface, and consequently, the coefficients of the second quadratic form of the surface $r = r(u, v)$ are equal to

$$\xi_u \cdot \zeta, \quad \xi_v \cdot \zeta, \quad \eta_v \cdot \zeta.$$

Taking into consideration the expressions for the derivatives $\xi_u,$ ξ_v and η_v in terms of ξ, η, ζ and the relations $\xi \cdot \zeta = 0, \eta \cdot \zeta = 0,$ $\zeta^2 = 1$, we have

$$\xi_u \cdot \zeta = L, \quad \xi_v \cdot \zeta = M, \quad \eta_v \cdot \zeta = N.$$

Hence, the surface thus constructed has

$$L\,du^2 + 2M\,dudv + N\,dv^2$$

as its second quadratic form.

The existence of a surface with prescribed first and second quadratic forms has thus been proved.

We shall now prove the uniqueness, to within position in space, of such a surface.

Suppose Φ_1 and Φ_2 are two surfaces whose first and second quadratic forms coincide. We shall associate the surfaces Φ_1 and Φ_2 by means of two corresponding points (e.g. by points corresponding to the same values of the parameters, say (u_0, v_0)), with the corresponding directions and normals. Such a correspondence is possible in virtue of the fact that the first quadratic forms coincide. Suppose $r = r_1(u, v)$ and $r = r_2(u, v)$ are the equations of the surfaces after such a correspondence.

The system of differential equations in ξ, η, ζ obviously is satisfied if we take

$$\xi = r_{1u}, \quad \eta = r_{1v}, \quad \zeta = n_1$$

or

$$\xi = r_{2u}, \quad \eta = r_{2v}, \quad \zeta = n_2.$$

And since both these solutions coincide at the point (u_0, v_0), they coincide identically. Hence,

$$r_{1u}(u, v) = r_{2u}(u, v), \quad r_{1v}(u, v) = r_{2v}(u, v)$$

or

$$dr_1(u, v) = dr_2(u, v).$$

It follows that

$$r_1(u, v) = r_2(u, v) + c.$$

Since $r_1 = r_2$ when $u = u_0$, $v = v_0$, we have $c = 0$ and, consequently, $r_1(u, v) = r_2(u, v)$.

Thus, the surfaces Φ_1 and Φ_2 are indentical, to within position in space.

This completes the proof of the theorem.

PROBLEMS AND THEOREMS FOR CHAPTER VIII

1_1. Show that if the linear element of a surface is

$$ds^2 = \lambda(du^2 + dv^2),$$

then the Gaussian curvature of the surface is

$$K = -\frac{1}{2\lambda} \Delta \ln \lambda,$$

where $\varDelta$ is the Laplace operator

$$\varDelta = \left(\frac{\partial^2}{\partial u^2} + \frac{\partial^2}{\partial v^2} \right).$$

1_2. Show that the surface with linear element

$$ds^2 = \frac{du^2 + dv^2}{(u^2 + v^2 + c)^2}$$

has constant Gaussian curvature.

2_1. Show that if the linear element of a surface has the form

$$ds^2 = du^2 + 2 \cos \omega \, dudv + dv^2,$$

then the Gaussian curvature of the surface is

$$K = \frac{\omega_{uv}}{\sin \omega}.$$

2_2. Prove that an arbitrary Chebyshevian net in a plane is defined by the vector equation

$$r = \varphi(u) + \psi(v).$$

The curves $u = $ constant and $v = $ constant form the net.

3. Find the Christoffel symbols $\varGamma_{ij}{}^k$ for the case when the linear element of the surface has the form

$$ds^2 = \lambda(du^2 + dv^2).$$

4_1. Show that if the coordinate net on a surface is asymptotic, then the following equalities are satisfied:

$$\tfrac{1}{2}(EG - F^2)(\ln K)_u + FE_v - EG_u = 0,$$

$$\tfrac{1}{2}(EG - F^2)(\ln K)_v + FG_u - GF_v = 0,$$

where K is the Gaussian curvature of the surface.

4_2. Prove that the asymptotic curves on a surface with constant negative curvature form a Chebyshevian net. And, conversely, if the asymptotic net on a surface is Chebyshevian, then the Gaussian curvature of the surface is constant.

5_1. If the coordinate net on a surface consists of lines of curvature, then the Peterson-Codazzi formulas assume the form

$$L_v = HE_v,$$
$$N_u = HG_u,$$

where H is the mean curvature of the surface. Show this.

5_2. If, on a minimal surface, one takes the lines of curvature as coordinate curves, and chooses the parameters u and v for the corresponding images, then the first and second quadratic forms assume the form

$$I = \lambda(du^2 + dv^2),$$
$$II = du^2 - dv^2.$$

Prove this assertion.

5_3. Suppose coordinates u, v are introduced on a minimal surface as in Exercise 5_2. Prove successively the following assertions:

a) if $r(u, v)$ is the position vector of a point on the surface, then

$$\Delta r = 0,$$

where Δ is the Laplace operator. Thus, the coordinates $x(u, v)$, $y(u, v)$, $z(u, v)$ of the vector $r(u, v)$ are harmonic functions;

b) if $f_1(w)$, $f_2(w)$, $f_3(w)$ ($w = u + iv$) are analytic functions with real part $x(u, v)$, $y(u, v)$, $z(u, v)$ respectively, then

$$f_1'^2 + f_2'^2 + f_3'^2 = 0.$$

5_4. If $f_1(w)$, $f_2(w)$, $f_3(w)$ are three arbitrary analytic functions of the variable $w = u + iv$, satisfying the condition

$$f_1'^2 + f_2'^2 + f_3'^2 = 0$$

and $\varphi_1(u, v)$, $\varphi_2(u, v)$, $\varphi_3(u, v)$ are the real parts of these functions, then the surface defined by the equations

$$x = \varphi_1(u, v), \quad y = \varphi_2(u, v), \quad z = \varphi_3(u, v),$$

is minimal. Prove this.

5_5. Prove that any minimal surface can be defined by the equations

$$z = Re \int (\varphi^2(w) + \psi^2(w))dw, \quad y = Re\, i \int (\varphi^2(w) - \psi^2(w))dw,$$
$$z = Re \int 2i\varphi(w)\psi(w)dw,$$

where φ and ψ are analytic functions of $w = u + iv$, and Re denotes the real part.

CHAPTER IX

INTRINSIC GEOMETRY OF SURFACES

Intrinsic geometry of a surface is that branch of geometry in which we study the properties of surfaces and figures on them which depend only on the length of curves on the surface. With respect to regular surfaces one can say that their intrinsic geometry studies the properties of the surfaces and figures on them which are defined by the first quadratic form.

To the realm of intrinsic geometry belong length of curves on a surface, the angle between curves, areas of regions, and the Gaussian curvature of a surface.

In the present chapter we shall consider new concepts for surfaces which are related only to its first quadratic form and thus belong to the intrinsic geometry of the surface.

§ 1. Geodesic curvature of a curve on a surface. Suppose Φ is a regular surface and that γ is a curve on Φ. We draw the tangent plane α to the surface at an arbitrary point P of the curve γ and we then project a small neighborhood of the point P on the curve γ onto this plane. Then we obtain some curve $\bar{\gamma}$ in the plane α. The curvature of $\bar{\gamma}$ at the point P is called the *geodesic curvature* of the curve γ at the point P. The geodesic curvature at the point P is assumed to be positive or negative depending on whether the rotation of the tangent to the curve $\bar{\gamma}$ in passing through the point P gives rise to a right or left screw in comparison with the direction of the normal to the curve at P. We shall find the expression for the geodesic curvature of the curve.

We draw a cylindrical surface through the curve γ with generators perpendicular to the plane α. By the Meusnier theorem the curvature k of the curve at the point P and the curvature κ of the curve $\bar{\gamma}$ at the same point are connected by the relation

$$k \cos \vartheta = \kappa,$$

where ϑ is the angle formed by the principal normals to these curves.

Suppose $r = \tilde{r}(s)$ is the natural parametrization of the curve γ, $\tilde{\tau}$ and $\tilde{n}$ are the unit tangent and unit normal vectors to the curve γ, and that n is the unit normal vector to the surface. Then $\tilde{r}'' = k\tilde{n}$, $\tilde{\tau} \times n$ are directed along the normals to the curve $\tilde{\gamma}$ at the point P and, consequently, except for sign,

$$\kappa = k \cos \vartheta = (\tilde{r}'', \tilde{r}', n).$$

We now go over to an arbitrary parametrization of the curve γ. We have

$$\tilde{r}_s' = \tilde{r}_t' t_s' = \tilde{r}_t'(1/|\tilde{r}_t'|),$$
$$\tilde{r}_{ss}'' = \tilde{r}(1/|\tilde{r}_t'|^2) + \tilde{r}_t'(1/|\tilde{r}_t'|)_s'.$$

If we substitute the above expressions for $\tilde{r}_s'$ and $\tilde{r}_{ss}'$ into the formula for κ, we obtain

$$\kappa = (1/|\tilde{r}'|^{3/2})(\tilde{r}'', \tilde{r}', n),$$

where differentiation is with respect to the parameter t.

Suppose $r = r(u, v)$ is any regular parametrization of the surface in a neighborhood of the point P and let $u = u(t)$, $v = v(t)$ be the equation of the curve γ in a neighborhood of this point. Then

$$\tilde{r}(t) = r(u(t), v(t)),$$
$$\tilde{r}' = r_u u' + r_v v',$$
$$\tilde{r}'' = r_{uu} u'^2 + 2r_{uv} u' v' + r_{vv} v'^2 + r_u u'' + r_v v'' =$$
$$= (u'' + A)r_u + (v'' + B)r_v + Cn,$$

where

$$A = \Gamma_{11}{}^1 u'^2 + 2\Gamma_{12}{}^1 u' v' + \Gamma_{22}{}^1 v'^2,$$
$$B = \Gamma_{11}{}^2 u'^2 + 2\Gamma_{12}{}^2 u' v' + \Gamma_{22}{}^2 v'^2,$$
$$C = L u'^2 + 2M u' v' + N v'^2.$$

Substituting the expressions for $\tilde{r}'$ and $\tilde{r}''$ into the formula for κ and carrying out the simple computations we obtain

$$\kappa = \{\sqrt{EG-F^2}/(Eu'^2+2Fu'v'+Gv'^2)^{3/2}\}(u''v'-v''u'+Av'-Bu').$$

Since the quantities $\Gamma_{ij}{}^k$ are expressed in terms of the coefficients of the first quadratic form of the surface only, the geodesic curvature of the curve on the surface is determined by only the metric of the surface and, consequently, remains invariant under bending of the surface.

We shall find a formula for the geodesic curvature of the curve in the case when the first quadratic form is

$$I = du^2 + Gdv^2.$$

In this case, as was shown in § 2, Chapter VIII,

$$\Gamma_{11}{}^1 = 0, \qquad \Gamma_{11}{}^2 = 0,$$
$$\Gamma_{12}{}^1 = 0, \qquad \Gamma_{12}{}^2 = \tfrac{1}{2}G_u/G,$$
$$\Gamma_{22}{}^1 = -\tfrac{1}{2}G_u, \qquad \Gamma_{22}{}^2 = \tfrac{1}{2}G_v/G.$$

It follows that

$$A = -\tfrac{1}{2}G_u v'^2,$$
$$B = (G_u/G)u'v' + \tfrac{1}{2}(G_v/G)v'^2.$$

Consequently,

$$\kappa = \{\sqrt{G}/(u'^2 + Gv'^2)\}\{u''v' - v''u' - \tfrac{1}{2}G_u v'^3 - $$
$$- \tfrac{1}{2}(G_v/G)u'v'^2 - (G_u/G)u'^2v'\}.$$

§ 2. Geodesic curves on a surface.

A curve on a surface is said to be a *geodesic curve* if its geodesic curvature vanishes at each of its points. We note two simple properties of geodesics.

1. If two surfaces are tangent along some curve γ which is a geodesic curve on one of the surfaces then γ will also be a geodesic curve on the other surface. This follows from the fact that the geodesic curvature of the curve will be the same independently of the surface we consider this curve to be on.

2. A necessary condition that the curve γ be a geodesic curve is that the osculating plane to the curve γ be perpendicular to the tangent plane to the surface at every point where the curvature of the curve γ does not vanish. In fact, the curvature k of the curve γ is connected with its geodesic curvature κ by the relation $k \cos \vartheta = \kappa$.

It follows that a necessary condition for γ to be a geodesic is that $\cos \vartheta = 0$ for $k \neq 0$, which means that the osculating plane to the curve is perpendicular to the tangent plane to the surface.

In order to obtain the differential equation of the geodesics, it suffices to set the expression for geodesic curvature equal to zero. Thus, the differential equation of the geodesics is

$$u''v' - v''u' + Av' - Bu' = 0.$$

THEOREM. *A unique geodesic can be drawn in any direction through every point on a regular surface.*

PROOF. Suppose $P(u_0, v_0)$ is any point on the surface and suppose $(u_0' : v_0')$ is an arbitrary direction at this point.

We consider the following system of differential equations

$$u'' + A = 0, \quad v'' + B = 0.$$

Suppose $u = u(t)$ and $v = v(t)$ is the solution of this system, satisfying the initial conditions

$$u(t_0) = u_0, \quad v(t_0) = v_0, \quad u'(t_0) = u_0', \quad v'(t_0) = v_0'.$$

Then the curve on the surface, defined by the equations

$$u = u(t), \quad v = v(t),$$

is a geodesic inasmuch as

$$u''v' - v''u' + Av' - Bu' = 0.$$

This geodesic passes through the point (u_0, v_0) and has the direction $(u_0' : v_0')$ at this point. We shall show that it is unique.

Suppose two geodesics γ_1 and γ_2 passing through the point (u_0, v_0) on the surface have the same direction $(u_0' : v_0')$. Suppose for definiteness that $u_0' \neq 0$. Then both curves can be defined by the following equations in a neighborhood of the point (u_0, v_0):

$$v = v_1(u), \quad v = v_2(u).$$

The condition that the geodesic curvatures of the curves γ_1 and γ_2 equal zero yields

$$- v_1'' + Av_1' - B = 0,$$
$$- v_2'' + Av_2' - B = 0.$$

Thus, the functions $v_1(u)$ and $v_2(u)$ satisfy the same differential equation with the same initial conditions

$$v_1(u_0) = v_0, \quad v_1'(u_0) = v_0'/u_0',$$
$$v_2(u_0) = v_0, \quad v_2'(u_0) = v_0'/u_0'.$$

From this it follows that $v_1(u) \equiv v_2(u)$, i.e. the curves γ_1 and γ_2 coincide in a neighborhood of the point (u_0, v_0) and, consequently, they coincide everywhere.

This complete the proof of the theorem.

§ 3. Semigeodesic parametrization of a surface. Suppose Φ is a regular surface and that γ is any regular curve on Φ which passes through the point P. Let $r = r(u, v)$ be any regular parametrization of the surface and let $u = u(t)$, $v = v(t)$ be a regular parametrization of the curve. Suppose the point P corresponds to the values u_0, v_0 and t_0 of the parameters.

We shall assume for definiteness that $v'(t_0) \neq 0$. We solve the equation $v = v(t)$ with respect to t in a neighborhood of (v_0, t_0). We obtain $t = t(v)$.

We now consider the family S of curves in a neighborhood of the point P, defined by the equations $u = u(t(v)) + c$ (c is a constant). The curve γ is a member of this family. As was shown in § 2, Chapter VI, the surface can be parametrized in a neighborhood of the point P in such a way that the curves of the family S and those of a family orthogonal to S will be coordinate curves. Suppose the surface is parametrized in precisely this way and let the curve γ have the equations $u = u_0$, $v = v(t)$.

We draw through the point (t) on the curve γ a geodesic γ_t in the direction perpendicular to the direction of the curve γ at this point. For t sufficiently close to t_0, the geodesics γ_t can be defined in a neighborhood of the point P by means of the equations

$$v = v(u, t)$$

where $v(u, t)$ is a function satisfying the equation of the geodesics with respect to u

$$- v'' + Av' - B = 0.$$

It follows from the theorem on the differentiability of the solutions of differential equations with given initial conditions that the function $v(u, t)$ is regular in t.

Differentiating the identity $v(t) = v(u_0, t)$ with respect to t and noting that $v'(t) \neq 0$, we conclude that $\dfrac{\partial}{\partial t} v(u_0, t) \neq 0$. This permits the solution of the equation $v = v(u, t)$ in a neighborhood of (u_0, v_0, t_0) with respect to t. We obtain

$$t = \varphi(u, v) \quad (\varphi_u{}^2 + \varphi_v{}^2 \neq 0).$$

This equation yields the geodesics γ_t in a neighborhood of the point P for t near t_0.

As was shown in § 2, Chapter VI, the surface can be parametrized in a neighborhood of the point P in such a way that one family of coordinate curves will be the curves $\varphi(u, v) = $ constant, and the second family will be perpendicular to the first. Such a parametrization of the surface is called *semigeodesic*.

We shall now discuss the first quadratic form of a surface if the parametrization is semigeodesic.

Since the parametrization is orthogonal, $F = 0$ and, consequently

$$I = Edu^2 + Gdv^2.$$

One family of coordinate curves, for example the curves $v = $ constant, are geodesics. Setting $v = $ constant into the equations for the geodesics

$$u''v' - v''u' + Av' - Bu' = 0$$

we obtain $B = 0$, from which we have

$$\Gamma_{11}{}^2 = -\tfrac{1}{2}E_v/G = 0,$$

i.e. E is independent of v.

Since E is independent of v, we can simplify the first quadratic form by introducing a new parameter $\bar{u}$ in place of u, where the new parameter is connected with u by the relation

$$d\bar{u} = \sqrt{E(u)}du.$$

Then the first quadratic form will be

$$I = d\bar{u}^2 + Gdv^2.$$

In order to understand the geometric interpretation of the parameter $\bar{u}$, it suffices to note that the length of the segment of any geodesic $v = $ constant, included between the curves $\bar{u} = c_1$, $\bar{u} = c_2$, does not depend on v and is equal to $|c_1 - c_2|$.

By introducing a new parameter $\bar{v}$, connected with v by the relation $d\bar{v} = \sqrt{\bar{G}(v, \bar{u}_0)}dv$, one can write the first quadratic form of the surface as

$$I = d\bar{u}^2 + \bar{G}(\bar{u}, \bar{v})d\bar{v}^2,$$

where $\bar{G} = 1$ along the curve $\bar{u} = u_0$.

If the curve $\bar{u} = u_0$ is also geodesic then it follows from the equation of the geodesics that $\bar{G}_u = 0$ along this curve.

§ 4. Shortest curves on a surface. A curve γ on a surface joining the points P and Q is called a *shortest curve* if any curve on the surface joining the points P and Q has length greater than or equal to the length of the curve γ.

THEOREM. *A geodesic on a sufficiently small segment is a shortest curve. More precisely, if γ is a geodesic and P is a point on it, and R and S are points on the geodesic, sufficiently close to P, then the segment RS on the geodesic is a shortest curve.*

PROOF. We draw through the point P the geodesic $\tilde{\gamma}$ which is perpendicular to γ and we construct a semigeodesic coordinate net, taking the geodesics perpendicular to $\tilde{\gamma}$ as the family of u-curves. We choose the parameters u and v so that the point P is assigned the values $u = v = 0$ and the linear element of the surface has the form

$$I = du^2 + Gdv^2.$$

We shall assume that the segment RS on the geodesic γ is not the shortest curve and that a curve $\tilde{\gamma}$ on the surface, joining the points R and S, has length less than the length of the segment RS on the geodesic γ.

If the points R and S are sufficiently close to P, the curve $\tilde{\gamma}$ passes through the interior of a neighborhood U_P of the point P, where the semigeodesic parametrization u, v is defined. We shall show this.

Since the form $du^2 + Gdv^2$ is positive definite, there exists an $\varepsilon > 0$ such that if $u^2 + v^2 < \varepsilon$ then

$$|r(u, v) - r(0, 0)| \geq k\sqrt{u^2 + v^2},$$

where k is a positive constant.

We shall now assume that the points R and S are so near the point P that their space distance from P is less than δ. Then if the curve $\tilde{\gamma}$ joining R and S passes outside the "circular disc" $u^2+v^2<\varepsilon$ into the point Q, then the length of $\tilde{\gamma}$ is, as is known, greater than $2k\varepsilon - 2\delta$. It suffices to equate the length of the curve $\tilde{\gamma}$ with the sum of the lengths of the rectilinear segments RQ and QS. We have come to a contradiction since the length of the segment RS on the geodesic γ tends to zero when $\delta \to 0$, and the length of the curve $\tilde{\gamma}$ is then bounded below by a positive number.

Hence, the curve $\tilde{\gamma}$ passes through the interior of the neighborhood U_P. In order to simplify the discussion, we shall assume that the curve $\tilde{\gamma}$ is piecewise smooth. Suppose $u = u(t)$, $v = v(t)$ is its equation. The length of the curve $\tilde{\gamma}$ is

$$s(\tilde{\gamma}) = \int\limits_{(R)}^{(S)} \sqrt{u'^2 + Gv'^2} \, dt \ge \int\limits_{(R)}^{(S)} |u'| dt \ge |u_S - u_R|.$$

But $|u_R - u_S|$ is the length of the segment RS on the geodesic γ. We have thus arrived at a contradiction.

This completes the proof of the theorem.

§ 5. The Gauss-Bonnet theorem.
Suppose G is a region, bounded by the closed piecewise regular curve γ, on a regular surface Φ. Assume G is homeomorphic to a circular disc. We shall direct the curve γ in such a way that by traversing the curve in this direction on that side of the surface toward which the normal n is directed, the region G remains on the right.

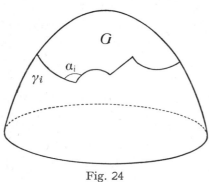

Fig. 24

We shall denote the geodesic curvature of the curve γ at an arbitrary point by κ, and $\alpha_1, \alpha_2, \cdots, \alpha_n$ will be the angles formed by the links $\gamma_1, \gamma_2, \cdots, \gamma_n$ of the curve γ on the side of the region G (Fig. 24). The following theorem holds.

THEOREM. *If K is the Gaussian curvature of the surface and the double integration is over the area of the region G, then*

$$\sum_k \int_{\gamma_k} \kappa ds + \sum_k (\pi - \alpha_k) = 2\pi - \iint_G K d\sigma.$$

In particular, if γ is a regular curve, then

$$\oint_\gamma \kappa ds = 2\pi - \iint_G K d\sigma.$$

PROOF. For simplicity of discussion, we shall assume that the curve γ is regular and that a semigeodesic parametrization of the surface can be introduced in the entire region G.

Taking into consideration the formula for geodesic curvature of the curve in semigeodesic coordinates, obtained in § 1, we shall have

$$\kappa ds = \frac{\sqrt{G}}{(u'^2+Gv'^2)}\left(u''v'-v''u'-\tfrac{1}{2}G_u v'^3-\tfrac{1}{2}\frac{G_v}{G}u'v'^2-\frac{G_u}{G}u'^2v'\right)dt =$$

$$= -\, d\, \arctan\frac{\sqrt{G}v'}{u'} - v'(\sqrt{G})_u dt.$$

Since the function *arctan* is multiple valued and its values corresponding to the same value of the argument differ by multiples of π, we have

$$\oint_\gamma - d \arctan \sqrt{G}v'/u' = k\pi,$$

where k is some integer.

Furthermore, by Ostrogradsky's formula, we have

$$\oint_\gamma -(\sqrt{G})_u dv = \iint_G (\sqrt{G})_{uu} du\,dv = \iint_G \frac{(\sqrt{G})_{uu}}{\sqrt{G}}\sqrt{G}\,du\,dv =$$

$$= \iint_G - K d\sigma.$$

Thus, we have

$$\oint_\gamma \kappa ds = k\pi + \iint_G - K d\sigma.$$

It remains to explain why k is an integer.

We have

$$k\pi = \oint_\gamma - d \arctan \sqrt{G}v'/u'.$$

If G were equal to 1, then the quantity $k\pi$ would be an angle through which the tangent to the curve $\bar\gamma$ in the u, v-plane corresponding to the curve γ on the surface rotates as it traverses this curve. The magnitude of this angle, as is known, equals 2π.

Since the value of the integral

$$\oint_\gamma - d \arctan \frac{\lambda(u,\,v)v'}{u'} \qquad (\lambda(u,\,v) > 0)$$

depends continuously on $\lambda(u,\,v)$ and equals 2π for $\lambda(u,\,v) = 1$, it equals 2π for any function $\lambda(u,\,v) > 0$, and in particular, for $\lambda(u,\,v) = \sqrt{G}$.

This completes the proof of the theorem.

A region on a surface is called a *geodesic triangle* if it is bounded by three geodesics and is homeomorphic to a circular disc.

The Gauss-Bonnet theorem, applied to a geodesic triangle, yields

$$\alpha + \beta + \gamma = \pi + \iint_{\Delta} K d\sigma.$$

From this it follows that the sum of the angles of a geodesic triangle on a surface with positive curvature is greater than π, on a surface with negative curvature it is less than π, and on a surface with zero curvature it is equal to π.

§ 6. Surfaces with constant Gaussian curvature.

Suppose Φ is a surface with constant Gaussian curvature K and that P is any point on Φ. We introduce a semigeodesic parametrization on Φ in a neighborhood of the point P, starting with an arbitrary geodesic which passes through P. The first quadratic form of the surface will be

$$I = du^2 + G dv^2,$$

where it can be assumed that $G(0, v) = 1$ and $G_u(0, v) = 0$.

Since the Gaussian curvature of the surface is constant and equal to K, the coefficient G must satisfy the differential equation

(*) $$(\sqrt{G})_{uu} + K\sqrt{G} = 0.$$

(In the case of a semigeodesic parametrization of the surface, the Gaussian curvature is $K = -(\sqrt{G})_{uu}/(\sqrt{G})$.)

We shall distinguish three cases: a) $K > 0$, b) $K < 0$, c) $K = 0$.

In the first case, the general form of $\sqrt{G}$ which satisfies equation (*) will be

$$\sqrt{G} = A(v) \cos \sqrt{K} u + B(v) \sin \sqrt{K} u.$$

Since $G(0, v) = 1$ and $G_u(0, v) = 0$, we have $A(v) = 1$ and $B(v) = 0$. Thus, in the case $K > 0$ there exists a parametrization of the surface for which the first quadratic form is

$$I = du^2 + \cos^2 \sqrt{K} u dv^2.$$

Analogously, in the second case, the first quadratic form of the surface is

$$I = du^2 + \cosh^2 \sqrt{-K} u dv^2.$$

Finally, in the third case, we have

$$I = du^2 + dv^2.$$

THEOREM. *All surfaces with constant Gaussian curvature K are locally isometric. Moreover, if Φ_1 and Φ_2 are surfaces with constant Gaussian curvature K, P_1 and P_2 are any points on these surfaces, l_1 and l_2 are arbitrary directions at these points, then there exists an isometric mapping of a neighborhood of the point P_1 on the surface Φ_1 onto a neighborhood of the point P_2 on the surface Φ_2, for which the direction l_2 on the surface Φ_2 at the point P_2 corresponds to the direction l_1 on the surface Φ_1 at the point P_1.*

To prove this theorem it suffices to introduce a semigeodesic parametrization in neighborhoods of the points P_1 and P_2 on the surfaces Φ_1 respectively Φ_2 starting with the geodesic directions l_1 and l_2. In this connection, the first quadratic forms of the surfaces will be the same, and the required isometric mapping is obtained by setting points with the same coordinates into correspondence.

PROBLEMS AND THEOREMS FOR CHAPTER IX

1. Show that if a geodesic curve is also an asymptotic curve then it is a straight line.

Show that if a geodesic is also a line of curvature then it is a plane curve.

2. Suppose γ is a geodesic and that P is a point on γ. Prove that if a point Q on the geodesic is sufficiently close to P, then the segment PQ on γ will be a shortest curve in comparison with all the rectifiable curves (and not only with the piecewise smooth curves) which join the points P and Q on the surface.

Prove that the segment PQ on the geodesic γ is the only shortest curve, joining the points P and Q on the surface, if the point Q is sufficiently close to P.

3. Prove that a point P on a regular surface has a neighborhood in which a semigeodesic parametrization can be introduced starting with any geodesic which passes through P.

4. Using the two preceding theorems, prove that any shortest curve on a regular surface is a geodesic.

5. Prove the whatever the neighborhood Ω of the point P on a regular surface one can always find a neighborhood ω in Ω such

that any two points in the neighborhood ω can be joined by a shortest curve in the interior of Ω.

6. Prove that on a complete surface any two points can be joined by a shortest curve.

7. Show that the equation of geodesics in the case of semigeodesic parametrization ($ds^2 = du^2 + Gdv^2$) can be written in the form

$$\frac{d\alpha}{dv} = -\frac{\partial\sqrt{G}}{\partial u},$$

where α is the angle at which the geodesics intersect the curves $v = $ constant.

8. Show that if the curve γ on a surface defined by the equations $u = u(\alpha)$, $v = v(\alpha)$, undergoes a deformation and goes over at time t into the curve $u = u(\alpha) + \lambda(\alpha)t$, $v = v(\alpha) + \mu(\alpha)t$, then the variation of the arc of the curve γ subjected to this condition is

$$\Delta s = t\int_{\gamma}\left(\frac{\partial\Phi}{\partial u}\lambda + \frac{\partial\Phi}{\partial v}\mu + \frac{\partial\Phi}{\partial u'}\lambda' + \frac{\partial\Phi}{\partial v'}\mu'\right)d\alpha + O(t^2),$$

where $\Phi = (Eu'^2 + 2Fu'v' + Gv'^2)^{\frac{1}{2}}$ and $O(t^2)$ denotes the part of Δs having order greater than or equal to t^2.

Carrying out the integration by parts and assuming that the endpoints of the curve γ remain fixed under the deformation, show that

$$\Delta s = t\int_{\gamma}\left(\frac{\partial\Phi}{\partial u} - \frac{d}{d\alpha}\left(\frac{\partial\Phi}{\partial u'}\right)\right)\lambda d\alpha + t\int_{\gamma}\left(\frac{\partial\Phi}{\partial v} - \frac{d}{d\alpha}\left(\frac{\partial\Phi}{\partial v'}\right)\right)\mu d\alpha + O(t^2).$$

9. Taking the property of geodesics of being shortest curves on a sufficiently small portion of a surface as point of departure, show that the equations of the geodesics can be written in the form

$$\frac{\partial\Phi}{\partial u} - \frac{d}{d\alpha}\left(\frac{\partial\Phi}{\partial u'}\right) = 0, \qquad \frac{\partial\Phi}{\partial v} - \frac{d}{d\alpha}\left(\frac{\partial\Phi}{\partial v'}\right) = 0,$$

where $\Phi = (Eu'^2 + 2Fu'v' + Gv'^2)^{\frac{1}{2}}$. In particular, if

$$\Phi = \sqrt{1 + Gv'^2},$$

the equation of the geodesics will be

$$\frac{\frac{1}{2}G_v v'^2}{\sqrt{1 + Gv'^2}} - \frac{d}{du}\left(\frac{Gv'}{\sqrt{1 + Gv'^2}}\right) = 0.$$

10. Show that the geodesic curves on a surface of revolution can be found by quadratures.

11_1. Show that the equations of geodesics for surfaces with linear element

$$ds^2 = (U(u) + V(v))(du^2 + dv^2)$$

(these surfaces are called Liouville surfaces) can be written in the form

$$d\left(\frac{U dv^2 - V du^2}{du^2 + dv^2}\right) = 0.$$

It follows from this that the geodesic curves on Liouville surfaces are found by quadratures. Namely, we have

$$\int \frac{du}{\sqrt{U - c}} = \pm \int \frac{dv}{\sqrt{V + c}} + c_1.$$

11_2. Prove that second degree surfaces are Liouville surfaces. The coordinate net, with respect to which the linear element has the form

$$ds^2 = (U + V)(du^2 + dv^2),$$

consists of lines of curvature (see Problem 9_3, Chapter VII).

12_1. Show that in a neighborhood of an arbitrary point P on a regular surface one can introduce a semigeodesic parametrization u, v, which is distinguished as follows. The u-curves are geodesics passing through the point P, and the v-curves are geodesic circumferences with center P. If the parameters are taken as u, the geodesic distance from P, and v, the angle formed by the geodesic with some fixed direction at the point P, then the linear element on the surface assumes the form

$$ds^2 = du^2 + G dv^2.$$

When $u \to 0$, $G \to 0$, $(\sqrt{G})_u \to 1$, $-\dfrac{(\sqrt{G})_{uu}}{\sqrt{G}} \to K(P)$, where $K(P)$ is the Gaussian curvature at P.

12_2. Suppose $l(r)$ is the length of the geodesic circumference with center at the point P on the surface and radius r. Prove that

$$\lim_{r \to 0} \frac{2\pi r - l(r)}{r^3} = \frac{\pi}{3} K(P),$$

where $K(P)$ is the Gaussian curvature at the point P.

13. Show that the geodesic curves on a surface with linear element

$$ds^2 = \frac{du^2 + dv^2}{(u^2 + v^2 + c)^2}$$

are

$$\alpha u + \beta v + \gamma = 0 \quad (\alpha,\ \beta,\ \gamma \text{ are constants}).$$

14_1. Show that the equation

$$- v'' + \frac{\varphi_{vv}}{\varphi_u}\, v'^3 + \frac{2\varphi_{uv}}{\varphi_u}\, v'^2 + \frac{\varphi_{uu}}{\varphi_u}\, v' = 0$$

is satisfied by

$$v = c_1\varphi + c_2 \quad (c_1,\ c_2 \text{ are constants}).$$

14_2. Show that if the equation of the geodesics in semigeodesic coordinates

$$v'' + \tfrac{1}{2}Gv'^3 - \tfrac{1}{2}\frac{G_v}{G}\, v'^2 + \frac{G_u}{G}\, v' = 0$$

has an integral of the form

$$v = c_1\varphi(u,\ v) + c_2,$$

where c_1 and c_2 are arbitrary constants, then $G = U(u)V(v)$, and, consequently, the Gaussian curvature of a surface along a v-curve is constant.

14_3. The mapping of one surface onto another is said to be geodesic if under this mapping the geodesics of one surface correspond to the geodesics on the other. It follows from Problems 1_2, Chapter VIII, and 13, Chapter IX, that surfaces with constant Gaussian curvature permit geodesic mappings onto a plane.

Prove that the only surfaces which possess this property are those with constant Gaussian curvature (Beltrand's theorem).

15_1. Suppose two points A and B are taken on the geodesic γ passing near the point O on a surface; suppose ϑ is the angle of the geodesic triangle AOB at the vertex O and that α is the corresponding angle of the plane triangle with the corresponding sides. Show that

$$\frac{\vartheta - \alpha}{\sigma} = \tfrac{1}{3}K^*,$$

where σ is the area of the geodesic triangle and K^* approximates the

Gaussian curvature of the surface at the point O, if the triangle is sufficiently small.

15_2. Suppose Δ is a geodesic triangle, containing the point P, on a surface. Suppose ϑ_1, ϑ_2, ϑ_3 are the angles of this triangle and that α_1, α_2, α_3 are the angles of the corresponding plane triangle (see the preceding problem). Prove that the three ratios

$$\frac{\vartheta_1 - \alpha_1}{\sigma}, \quad \frac{\vartheta_2 - \alpha_2}{\sigma}, \quad \frac{\vartheta_3 - \alpha_3}{\sigma}$$

tend to the common limit $\frac{1}{3}K(P)$ when the triangle Δ shrinks to the point P (Darboux's theorem).

16. The surfaces F_1 and F_2 are called the surfaces of centers of the surface F if they are formed by the endpoints of segments of lengths $1/k_1$ and $1/k_2$ (k_1 and k_2 are the principal curvatures of F), marked off on the normals to the surface F. A point correspondence is established in a natural way between the surfaces F_1, F_2 and F. Namely, points on the surfaces lying on the same normal to F are corresponding points. Prove that geodesic curves on the surfaces of centers correspond to lines of curvature on the surface F.

BIBLIOGRAPHY

W. BLASCHKE. *Vorlesungen über Differentialgeometrie*, Springer, Berlin, 3rd ed., 1930.

W. BLASCHKE, *Einführung in die Differentialgeometrie*, Springer, Berlin, 1950.

L. EISENHART. *An Introduction to Differential Geometry with the use of the Tensor Calculus*, Princeton University Press, Princeton, 1940.

W. GRAUSTEIN. *Differential Geometry*, Macmillan, New York, 1935.

J. HAANTJES. *Inleiding tot de Differentiaalmeetkunde*, Noordhoff, Groningen-Djakarta, 1954.

G. JULIA. *Eléments de Géométrie Infinitésimale*, Gauthier-Villars, Paris, 2nd ed., 1936.

E. LANE. *Metric Differential Geometry of Curves and Surfaces*, University of Chicago Press, Chicago, 1940.

A. NORDEN. *Differential Geometry* (Russian), Uchpedgiz, Moscow, 1948.

A. NORDEN. *Theory of Surfaces* (Russian), Gosudarstv. Izdat. Teh.-Teor. Lit., Moscow, 1956.

P. RASHEVSKY. *Course in Differential Geometry* (Russian), Gostehizdat., Moscow-Leningrad, 3rd ed., 1950.

D. STRUIK. *Lectures on Classical Differential Geometry*, Addison-Wesley, Reading, 1950.

C. WEATHERBURN. *Differential Geometry of Three Dimensions*, University Press, Cambridge, I, 1927; II, 1930.

INDEX